Sisters

IMPRINT

Sisters

EDITED BY DRUSILLA MODJESKA

Angus&Robertson
An imprint of HarperCollins*Publishers*

An Angus & Robertson Publication

Angus&Robertson, an imprint of
HarperCollins*Publishers*
25 Ryde Road, Pymble, Sydney, NSW 2073, Australia
31 View Road, Glenfield, Auckland 10, New Zealand
10 East 53rd Street, New York NY 10022, USA

First published in Australia in 1993
Reprinted in 1993 (four times)

National Library of Australia
Cataloguing-in-Publication data:

Sisters.

   ISBN 0 207 17790 2.

   1. Short stories, Australian.
   I. Modjeska, Drusilla.

A823.0108

Cover photograph of Elizabeth Jolley and her sister,
Madelaine Blackmore, taken in 1929.
Courtesy The State Library of NSW.
Printed in Australia by Griffin Paperbacks, Adelaide.

10 9 8 7 6 5
96 95 94 93

CONTENTS

INTRODUCTION

DRUSILLA MODJESKA

S isters are not easy to write about. Consider Janet Frame's achievement in telling the story of the day her sister Myrtle drowned. That day, like so many others, Myrtle and Janet had quarrelled. Myrtle had wanted Janet to go to the baths with her, and on into town to look at the boys; Janet had wanted to stay at home with her lessons and her books. Myrtle accused her of being 'Dad's pet', and it was true, Janet curried favour where Myrtle flouted and rebelled, each defining the other against the definition made of herself in a complex dance of inclusion and exclusion. So Myrtle went to the baths that day with the other sister; and Janet was at home when the doctor called to tell their mother that Myrtle was dead. In this brief, unforgettable chapter of her autobiography, Janet Frame brings to us in loss an acute understanding of the complicated, uneven tide of lived feeling that passes between girls who share parents: rivalry and resentment, sensitivity to slights and differences, tears and tantrums, dreams and fantasies, and love as abiding as blood.

The contributors to this book were given a simple brief: to write about the vexed relationship between sisters in any way, in any form, they liked: essay, fiction, autobiography. All six of us have sisters. Elizabeth Jolley and Dorothy Hewett are both the elder of two. Helen Garner is the eldest of five – and has one brother. (*We love him, and we're proud of him*, she writes. *But he belongs to the male strand of the family: a different species.*) I am the eldest of three. Gillian Mears is third of four, and Beth Yahp the second of four. There was no shortage of material for this juicy task. Everyone accepted eagerly, or at least willingly; and all of us were caught short by how hard it proved: for reasons that have to do less with writing than with the nature of sisters. Is there anyone as hurtful and infuriating, anyone who can cast greater prohibitions? Not that it was a case of overt prohibition. The anxiety was ours; and anyone who doubts that the consequences can be dire when sister breaches the trust of sister should read A.S. Byatt's early novel *The Game*, in which the novelist sister exposes (and ridicules) the early love of her now middle-aged, donnish sister.

On a less dramatic scale, every sister knows what it is when the other (or others) won't speak to her. Sisters are good at punishment, and they have long memories. It's one thing to grumble in private, another to tell your sister face to face; yet another to have her see it in print. And for those of us who are the eldest, there is also the desire to protect, and the temptation to direct, to organise, to *tell*. It was with mesmerised fascination that I read the pieces by Beth Yahp and Gillian Mears: those younger sisters describing bossy, demanding, overly capable, busy, all-too-recognisable big sisters.

Not that these essays and stories are filled with criticisms and dobbings in. On the contrary, pride, pleasure, a connection that can only be named as love shines through them all: genuinely so. But if that were all, if that were the only chord we struck, we'd be serving up *glossy lies*. That was the phrase Helen Garner used in a letter describing her search for a form that would be 'meaty and hilarious' but wouldn't get her into trouble. The strategy she hit on was to interview her sisters and to juxtapose their voices in what she calls 'A Scrapbook, An Album'. That way she could avoid the tyranny of a single point of view which, in the case of an eldest sister, runs the risk of adding insult to injury: for the eldest is, by virtue of her place and position, best situated to control the competing myths and stories by which families live. The result, her scrapbook, her album, *is* hilarious. And very meaty.

When I read it, and also Gillian Mears' 'The Childhood Gland', I was filled with a sorrowful amazement. Both describe a present life in which sisters live closely. In Helen Garner's case all five sisters live in Melbourne; they go shopping together in different combinations, they go to films and bands and choir practice. Gillian Mears and her sisters are scattered between northern New South Wales and southern Queensland, but they are still a gang, *the Mears girls*, and no one else ever quite cuts the mustard. They are each other's champions, and they are friends. Perhaps for this reason she has, more than anyone else, been able to write in a directly autobiographical voice. Not that there is an absence of tensions, or shifting allegiances, or dreadful things said by one behind another's back. *We scar easily and remember everything*, she writes. But when in the past she has written of fictional sisters, giving them different accents and landscapes, she's overcome, she says, with *a sense of phoniness*. Only real sisters will do. So she goes the whole hog, and the result is marvellous.

This sort of close contact with one's sister is strange to me— at once alarming and enviable. I have lived all my adult life on the other side of the world from my sisters, separated by oceans, meridians, hemispheres. I see them on visits to England. My middle sister and her family once lived here, in Sydney, for a couple of years, but it wasn't enough for us to learn such intense intimacies. She had a family of young children and I was writing a book. We had to create the points at which our lives intersected. Much as I loved her being here, the tenor of my adult life has always been lived away from both of them, *somewhere else*. So when I wrote my piece, 'The Cuckoo Clock', it didn't occur to me to write about now, about our lives in the present, except in the lightest of ways, but about childhood and its stories and memories that never seem to match up. My strategy of avoidance was to press into service once more the parallel family, not mine, yet like mine, that I invented for *Poppy*.

Beth Yahp has also lived her adult life without any sisters on the same land mass. She writes about visiting the eldest in London, the one she was paired with, the one who focused and demanded her attention as a child, and was the first to leave Malaysia, with Beth waving at the window, waiting her turn. In 'Houses, Sisters, Cities', her graceful meditation on the love and tyranny of an eldest sister, memory and childhood are the nexus for the trouble that begins when they grow up. There they are in London, grown women shopping for a wedding dress, yet still children in *the crush and swell* of the market; the smells and sounds of Malaysia come down the telephone wires with their mother's and each other's voices.

It is with Elizabeth Jolley and Dorothy Hewett that the distance between the sisters seems greatest; perhaps because the proportion of life lived outside the childhood family is greater than that lived within it. The distance is not one of feeling, far from it, nor of intimacy, nor immediacy; nor is it merely one of time and geographical space; it is to be found in the poise of the relationship that is established between the narrative 'I' and the autobiographical, or fictional, moment that is evoked. There is concision in the way the past is held simultaneously out there, in a time that has long gone, and here and now, in memory, and in the present moment of the writing.

Dorothy Hewett uses the Darkling sisters, a wholly imagined pair, to frame her own more personal musings. The dark story of 'The Darkling Sisters' which haunts the house and inspires the writing, falls as a shadow across the generations of sisters who inhabit Dorothy Hewett's own history. For Elizabeth Jolley it is the wonderful character of 'her' father, familiar to readers of her work, who gives a focus to the sharp images of memory in which generations, sisters, families, float. We are reminded that it is the sharing of parents that makes sisters of the girls born to them. Fathers especially, but mothers too, play their part in each of these essays and stories; only Helen Garner manages to minimise the father to a few lines, though as the sisters all know all too well, his presence still does its work underground. ' "Wait till your father dies," says somebody's husband. "You'll be like the Baltic states at the collapse of the Soviet Union." '

Elizabeth Jolley is the only one of the six of us to comment directly on the way in which the spiced incidents of childhood, the games played with her sister, and by her father and his sister, have found their way into her fiction, a sort of recycling of memory in the process of imagination and writing. It is for this reason that the collection ends with 'My Sister Dancing'. The book is arranged in reverse order of generational age. Gillian Mears and Beth Yahp, both still in their twenties, come first; Helen Garner and myself, in mid life, come next; and then Dorothy Hewett and Elizabeth Jolley with the insights that the perspective of their experience allows. As one uses fiction and the other comments on its processes, their stories, coming last, draw strands from the ones that go before, linking them to all the stories that have ever been written about sisters, for when all is said and done this book is less a collection of case studies on the vexations of sisters than exercises in writing, in telling, in remembering. It is a salute to those bright figures that are born *as gifts*, Elizabeth Jolley says, and though they may be divided from us by cities and states and countries, live on undimmed in the psyche: the gift, and the vexation, of sisters.

THE CHILDHOOD GLAND

GILLIAN MEARS

My sister holds out her hand to me. For a moment I think the white mice in her palm are sugar mice she has made using beaten egg white and icing-sugar. But they're my own dead. Paul and Paulette, I think I named them and only a few days before had sealed up the escape hole they'd gnawed in the fruitcase home that neither they nor I wanted. I cup my hands. Sonya tips in the bodies. She looks at me and her eyes are like watermelon seeds. My little sister's eyes make me cry. I try to pretend I'm crying for my mice that I've murdered through weeks of long malnutrition and general neglect, and Sonya isn't fooled. It is hard to pass a lie to a sister. On my hand the mice feel light and desiccated. My fake grief shines through as clearly as the pink light through their ears.

In the old kitchen that is Sonya's bedroom in the Miller Street house in Grafton, I hear Karin and Sonya talking. Not only do I hate the mouse project, they are saying, but the love I hold for my cat isn't anywhere in the league of love they experience for their dogs. I listen to the companionable noise of my sisters sharing a packet of dog chocolates which taste fine as long as they are straight from the fridge. These are the beginning of the sugar-deficient years, when our mother has begun to make health food cakes instead of sponges. The house, which used to be the Grafton ferryman's, where we live all our adolescent years, smells sour from the lichens that grow up it like it's a tree not a building. I stay a little longer to hear their pronouncements before trailing away to bury the mice under the frangipani outside our parents' bedroom window. Yvonne comes home on the old blue bike we imagine once belonged to the giantess of Grafton it is so tall and the seat so wide. I hear Yvonne fall off. She takes the steps three at a time. I hear her kick down Sonya and Karin's welcoming dogs. I stay hidden in the creamy shadows of the frangipani, digging graves with a stick.

It isn't so much that my sisters mind the mice are dead. They kill their own with scalpels stolen from school. The hostility comes from my approach to the project, which has been lukewarm from the first. As Karin, Yvonne and Sonya devote many hours to breeding, killing, dissecting and tanning the skins of their pet-charges, I've allowed my concentration to wane. I haven't been wholehearted enough. I've betrayed the sisterly allegiance system that binds us still, twelve or fifteen years on.

If I had an ordinary Australian grandma I would run round to her place but Eileen Challacombe is better. She makes me Yorkshire pudding and shows me the piglets just born and doesn't ask too many questions. She is our mother's only real friend. Her laugh happens deep in her throat like singing. I help Eileen fold damask serviettes. She helps our mother clean our house. Her son is flagrantly gay for such a small town and I love him silently for years, from afar, for his exquisite style. She shows me photo albums of her long-ago childhood in Shanghai and makes me forget the disgrace of having erred in the eyes of my sisters. *Margerie was my sister*, she says, showing me pictures of ringleted girls in frocks. *She was much more beautiful*. But no one is, no one could be. Eileen is quite old but she wears her steel grey hair in two long plaits that thump her back when she walks. And we tell each other this is exactly how we will be when we reach that age.

Red leather, yellow leather, red leather, yellow leather. Our project carries the tongue-twisting rhyme from language into production. Yvonne wants enough mouse-skin leathers to make quivers. She makes bows and arrows out of stinkwood and shoots down a magpie. *Redleatheryellowleatherred-*

leatheryellowleatherredleatheryellowleather. The tanning fluid is brewed using bark from the wattle trees in the back garden. We had a grandmother, we know, who went mad on a wattle plantation in South Africa. It's where the mouse-skin idea comes from. From one of the Natal Tanning Extract Company booklets in one of the old trunks. Betty was our father's mother. Our parents look for signs of her in us, all through childhood and beyond, waiting for a mad child to emerge. *Redleatheryellowleatherredleatheryellow.* Red is Karin's favourite colour, yellow Sonya's, green Yvonne's and mine is blue.

In Grafton there is nothing to do and our tongues grow thick with repetitions.

There is something brazen in the way I love my sisters. Yet sometimes, when I am overwhelmed by the extreme way I'm loved back, all I want is to run away. For a while at least, to not be a Mears Girl. Their number is growing. Sonya's boys began to call themselves Mears Girls, as if it is the name of a type of hero, and have to have it explained.

Perhaps it's because in the sixties, before the move to Grafton, there are four of us under the age of five. Or that our mother believes in reclusiveness to the extent that we're each other's only true friends and hers too.

When I see my sisters I hear how we tend to scream and yell. The noise rises around us faster than any flood. We don't act the way I've noticed other sisters act. We don't hug and kiss. The nieces call us the Indian Arm Wrestling Aunts. We shake hands. They all drive big old cars that burble, and live on hills where they can't be seen. We swap boots. My sisters laugh at the five hairs under my belly button and at my breasts, which remain the floppiest though they've done no baby feeding. *Yes*, they say, *you'll be enormous when you're in milk.* If Yvonne has a long grey hair hanging over her forehead, one of us will pull it free. We'll descend into each other's hair, searching for more signs of age. Because I am childless, is why I don't have any, they think. They suggest who'd be someone good to get sperm from. They can't imagine I won't follow them into motherhood and order me to hurry up about it. If I shut my eyes I can imagine three dazzling queen parrots screeching, as they sift through my hair. We can't hug and kiss and I still don't know why.

If one of us is absent we may find ourselves saying dreadful things about her.

We eat more sugar than the next generation of children. There are nine so far yet we are not Catholic or any religion particularly. I am the favourite aunt. The nieces carry around hexagons I've crocheted which they've stuffed with hair from my brush. They take their hair-hexagons to bed in order to have my smell with them when the visit is over. *Oh the buzzing of the bees and the cigarette trees, the soda water fountains.* I sing what our mother used to sing. There is so much noise I sing around a corner. Everyone is gabbling at once. My sisters sound like birds. It is one of the dangers of trying to write about them. That the details will disappear in the noise.

Our mother used to eat too much sugar too and dies when she is not old. But even as she's dying and we are easing her tongue with a grapefruit flavoured swab and her hat is tipped at a death angle to the pillow, we don't think she can die. She believes in her own invincibility and we do too. When we are little she teaches us how to make quick toffee, heating caster sugar in a pan over high heat. Teaspoons become lollipop sticks. Our mother has an English complexion and few wrinkles. Ours is Australian and when we're tired there are purple-coloured sockets under our eyes. In bright light we can all pass for a decade older than our true age. We scar easily and remember everything. A scratch will still be mulberry a year or more later.

Why will our faces no longer carry fat? I don't know. It's

our lantern jaws, Yvonne says, drawing how we'll look if we ever reach old age. She draws four thin skulls. When she was a child her series of monster paintings, which she'd hold down for me to see from the top bunk, gave me nightmares I still remember.

Our real faces are small. We all look like insects if we try to wear sunglasses and grow the same squint wrinkles instead. Our cheekbones make me remember the day our father's stockhorse mare smashed her head against the yards. We could see into her face through bones as fine and fragile as the plywood gliders our father used to buy us to construct and fly. I fainted seeing the eye pop out. Yvonne helped the vet hold it.

We have long arms and long necks. In jumpers, we roll up the sleeves to the elbow. There are muscles in our forearms. One day we'll have to bury a sister. I hope it's me.

Still we don't move. Our mother's calling her four daughters but we keep dipping our hands into a bucket of sunflower seed. The seeds are warm. The parrots wait in the figtree for us to move.

Although it's a golden afternoon we are no longer children and our mother, who's directing our father to cut down the first ripe pod of bananas, is dying. She's wearing a long dove-coloured dressing gown and a bonnet that makes the garden seem to be the set for a Chekhov play. It's calm weather, the last day of June; Sonya's birthday and she's a quarter of a century old.

– Sunflowers are like chocolate for parrots. Did you know, she says.

A memory of tossing Sonya into the air on my knees, arrives and leaves. White bells are ringing in a white Greek church that make our mother cry with pleasure. Memories that aren't photos. In Greece we live on baby sardines and Coca-Cola. Sonya was plumper then and that encouraged strangers to want to reach out and squeeze her. Once she was so tiny she could hide in the grandfather clock in the hall of the ferryman's house, pretending to chime. For her seventh birthday in Crete our mother bought her a sunflower cake. I think so anyway. In my memory our plates are awash with honey as Sonya unwraps a glass charm to ward off the evil eye. But I know I've always had a tendency to find links and connections where there aren't any – how can there be, when nearly twenty years have passed, we are not girls anymore and our mother is dying?

– Really? Like chocolate? says Karin.

I like how she says their wings seem to be red capes. She is heavily pregnant with her fourth baby, who will be called Little Sonya when she's born two weeks after our mother dies.

– Saturated fat. We're wrecking their livers.

Sonya rattles off facts but bites down on that one, because our mother has a kind of cancer that has moved quickly into her lungs and now her liver. She is calling out for us. Our father is sawing the soft banana wood. Her voice is still her clear English voice though now we remember how last year she would pause for a while if she'd walked up a hill. She'd hold her ribs and say hang on until I get my breath. Karin begins to throw the seed in arcs away from us.

– One day before I went to Africa, I say, she said she could see fireworks in her left eye. But she looked so *well*.

We concentrate a moment longer on the birds. It's safe out here in the garden and it's my little sister's birthday. I begin to recognize my fondness for that expression. My little sister, as if the tenderness it elicits cannot ever be overdone. Our mother's favourite dog has climbed onto the highchair in the sun and stares out across the river.

– If I lived here, says Yvonne, I'd net this fig tree in and write my stories under that.

Her real desk is a door on 44-gallon drums. Budgie wings and bones decorate its surface. Our father's gymnast rings as well as horse paraphernalia hang above. Her crow, Furious, sits watching her work and on each of Yvonne's shoulders are scars from crow claws. Sometimes Furious talks too much and she throws her outside. One day when I am in Yvonne's desk room (which smells of dark feathers and leather dressings), I see a picture of a beautiful woman. The piece of paper's folded over. Hmm, I think, what a beautiful and serene face the painted woman has.

– Well, says Yvonne, coming up behind me. What would you say she's looking at?

– Parchment? Perhaps.

Yvonne gives her manic laugh and unfolds the other side of the painting.

– Judith and Holofernes! she says.

I look down at a gory decapitation scene.

Yvonne is the eldest and the eldest girl in a family of sisters is always the fiercest. But go for a walk with Yvonne through any landscape and you will see things another way.

– So this is it, this is how it feels sometimes, she observes as our mother is dying. So peaceful and ordinary and unalarming.

– We should go over, I say, but still we stand. I tell my sisters I feel so immobilised I have dreams somebody keeps attaching me to a piece of string to fly me in an afternoon wind away from the hill.

– The air smells of straw, says one of us.

– It's storms and beetles, I reply.

– It's your hat, dumb-dumb.

– I smell citrus blossom.

Who says what doesn't always matter. Our voices are almost perfectly interchangeable, half Australian, half something else. Yvonne's goes faster, that's about the only difference.

– Gillian! There is the call for me. I've always been her favourite.

As we begin to move towards our mother, I notice we all

9

have our hair up. How stalky our necks seem, how vulnerable. Our arms look too long. This is the third house our parents have lived in in Australia and the thinnest. Only Sonya lived here for the tailend of her childhood. There's so much glass you can see clear through to the river. This sensation adds to the unreality of afternoons. In our reflections we seem to go all glittery with uncried pain.

I think how Yvonne used to make me do dangerous tricks in the late evening light. How I was her minion. It would grow late and dark but we'd continue to jump our horses over pieces of string or wire. It was like facing yourself and your horse at nothing. The impending death of our mother feels the same. There are no ground-lines, rules or precedents and the leap, though fully anticipated, will still come as a terrible surprise. I wish suddenly that I was ten years old again. When I was a child, right up until I was a late developing fifteen-year-old, I was so thin, so bendable, I could walk right under the belly of my mare, following the figure of my big sister wherever she might lead me.

I don't believe it's possible to write about my sisters without writing about our mother too. When we were teenagers, she called herself the fifth sister, but wistfully, knowing she wasn't really.

Through the action of tumours rubbing against her stomach lining, our mother's belly is as big as Karin's nearly full-term pregnancy. The irony is not ignored. Our mother has a string of jokes about full-term babies and often refers to her pain in terms relative to childbirth. Coffee brewed four rooms away causes her nausea.

Karin's life seems the closest to our mother's. Her place is on the edge of a small weatherboard town on a small rocky acreage. She has made a round rose garden, just as our mother did in the sixties, in a very similar northern landscape of empty paddocks and far blue rock candy peaks with edges so sharp they'd cut your tongue. A town hall tin chair in the middle of the circle is turning to rust. Karin sits there with the hose in her hand and there are many small children and dogs running past. Karin and I are the middle girls. The soft centres, our mother says, and we are. We are not as vehement or ferocious or relentless in the way we lead our lives.

– Darling? On my birthday, which is twenty-one days after Sonya's, our mother holds out her now tiny arms. The inscription she has written in the biography is without indication of the gravity of the situation. It's a polite far-feeling inscription. Sometimes, I say to Sonya in exasperation, it's as if she's approaching her own death in the way she used to read biographies: refusing to skip ahead or to look at the pictures before they are arrived at in the text.

I take her arms over my shoulders, waiting for her question before bending towards my knees. In the lift position our eyes can't ever meet and her fingers tap my back like wings. Yvonne comes to help. Our mother orders her away. Yvonne's eyes might as well be my own, the dismay I find in them is so sharp.

– I can't finish my letter with all of you flapping around me, our mother says. All of you, she says, meaning Yvonne, whom she is determined still to paint as a daughter tyrant. There are things at this point that can't be mentioned, that would crack our hearts to acknowledge.

On my birthday our mother is writing a letter on airmail paper with butterflies on the border. It is to her own mother but she has no intention of posting it. At times, the letter seems to cause her distress. She's writing out all her griefs and all the old hatreds. She can remember only two kindnesses, very ordinary ones, such as would've occurred to any one of us on any one day of our childhood. After sleeping on her accusations for a night, she burns them.

Our mother seems glad as well as gentler. One day, she advises me, when we feel ready, we should write out similar

11

letters of grievance. Against her. You can't be a mother, she says, of four girls, without inflicting damage.

For a number of days after my twenty-seventh birthday the remains of our mother's letter stay under a vase of flowers. The vase makes the rose stems look like dancers' legs, says Sonya. The rose stems dancing in spangled green tights. My fanciful little sister.

But the saucepan of ashes begins to unsettle us. Something has died in that saucepan, I think. The afternoons are so quiet we can hear the high tide slapping against the other side of the riverbank. Soon Yvonne and Karin will go back to Queensland and we have to battle the strong temptation to poke the ashes with a twig, to try to work out some of the unburnt words. It's a relief when our mother decides to bury them in a pot underneath some flowers. She can no longer bend so Sonya helps prepare the soil. It is late in the year to be putting in spring flowers but I like to think of the way the freesia bulbs will begin to send their shoots through bad memories; towards light.

My sisters' hands, when I shake them goodbye, are broad and padded, like workers' hands. Sometimes I am amazed when I look at the hands of other girls, to see how delicate they are. None of us have ever had our mother's hands. Whenever I see a sister after an absence I wonder why it's only our fingers and palms that are touching. Their hands are warm; mine are cold. They knuckle-crunch my fingers as if they are not mothers or grownups and never will be.

Sometimes we consult each other, trying to find the reasons. We blame our mother. We blame our father. We blame the madness that put fears of it repeating itself on a not very well hidden agenda.

In the ferryman's house there are shadows on the floor in summer. There is a man in our mother's bedroom who isn't our father. In Grafton summers are long and winters warm.

We all wander round with no clothes on. Our mother banishes our father to the cement bathroom downstairs. The shadows move slowly and take years to decipher. Even now these outlines of old stories seem as if they may never join up.

– I think it was dangerous trying to be friendly to a Mears girl.
  – Well, yes, in a way.
  – There was something sometimes monstrous.
  – Is!
(laughter)
  – Only in that we didn't need anybody else.
The voices don't matter. Our voices are all the same. Have I mentioned that? Yes. We are always repeating ourselves. Don't boil your cabbages, we tell each other. We still like to trick people sometimes. We can easily trick our father, who calls us by each other's names anyway, or sometimes by the name of a dog or cat long deceased.
We hedge people out.
People who are not sisters say things like: you all begin to act like ten-year-olds when you see each other.
  – A crowbar couldn't wedge you apart.
  – You're still little gels, aren't you Mummy, says Sonya's four-year-old.
I think it's our gland of childhood, says Karin, on the back of a postcard she has made of her shadow standing in a ploughed field. The shadow is tall and eerie. It takes me months to go in search of what she means.
  – Highschool biology, the thymus, you know, *The Web of Life*, Karin's voice over the phone sounds withering and then she has to hang up.
  – Sweethearts . . . I hear her voice rising from the middle of the noise, before the phone is put down.

Our mother cries in storms. She sees haloes around storm clouds and her own death occurring in a blaze of lightning.

Sometimes she cries if we laugh. On her way to Africa, during a storm at sea, she threw all her clothes out the porthole. She is always happy at the beach, in blue swimmers, floating in the shallows.

We grow up being careful not to make our mother cry. We can make her laugh and her laughter is infectious, but nothing we ever say or do can take away the sadness that gives her that smudged and stony kind of beauty. My sisters and I have our father's brown eyes but hers are pale. She hates that they are so deep set. We hate how she tries to smooth wings of eyeshadow out from their corners, using a mixture of blues, silver and mauve on her finger. She trusts no one, not us nor anyone I can remember. She holds her grudges forever. When she cries behind half-closed doors we know it's dangerous to look. After a certain age we aren't allowed to climb into her lap. She runs away twice and says if she kills herself it will be by drowning. The river in flood comes to within three feet of cresting the jetty and smells to us of death. Or is it the blood and bone melting down in the wind coming from the tannery on the other side of the river?

At other times, though she never hits us, she smashes china. Karin and I do also. What has been unleashed, I wonder? And what exactly do we do when she's throwing? When we are children? We learn more about invisibility. We eat sugar in our bedrooms, with our noses in books. We have fast metabolisms and are all speed readers. Only Yvonne tries to match our mother's anger with her own. They fight and cry and hate each other. Sweethearts, our mother calls us but there are times when we no longer believe her.

Our mother's anger chooses ancient and irreplaceable china. She throws downwards, so that the vase or bowl or thin Minton teacup moves through the shallowest of trajectories before shattering. Later, after moving to the farm, she has a throwing wall. She hurls her anger against it. One day far into the future, someone's going to end up with cuts all over their hands pulling out the old allamanda vine that grows against that wall, for it is my wall now, though I only ever throw bottles or vegemite jars. Sonya has a bottom drawer full of china she says she's going to mend one day. She's been saying this since she was seven years old.

I can remember my little sister in hand-me-down swimmers, crouched over the kitchen floor the summer after we came home from England. She is so brown her skin has a kind of gloss. She's searching for a piece of parrot head. She's been feeding her honey spiders which is why she's up at the house not down at the river where we spend most of our holidays. Her feet are bare and it seems remarkable to me they are not getting cut. 'Mummy's crying,' she says. I cock my head. Our mother cries all the time since we're back in Australia and we don't know why. For Christmas and her birthday we give her linen and cross-stitch hankies for her tears.

I shake my head. 'Come down and play sardines,' I say. 'Yvonne said to come and get you.'

Not that we'll play sardines. Instead Yvonne and Karin will get us with willow wand whips or we will get them. Or if it's summer, regardless of the deadly bullrout fish who live in the river weed, we'll press our bodies through there in order to continue the weed war we rage against our neighbours. Even our dog Rolf has been trained at a command to bash up their blue heeler Bernie. Sonya is tireless in building booby traps and has ambushed her room with logs that fall when you open her door.

'Here are The Babies,' says Karin, when we reach the pampas grass. Karin is about eleven, Yvonne twelve, I must be nine or ten, Sonya almost eight. It's the early seventies. Yvonne's drawing horses in the circle of white sand dumped by the last flood.

– I hated school, says Yvonne these days. It did me Untold Damage. Only near horses did I feel a hint of infinity.

Yvonne continues to draw horses. Not a day goes by when

she doesn't. They are her nemesis. There are her bony headed mares with their ears laid back and often accompanied now by naked women with highly muscled legs. When she draws me, I am always half mare.

– Is there such a thing as a female centaur, Gillian? she phones me after midnight to ask. She lives without sleep to fit in all she wants her life to be. Instead of drinking coffee, she eats sugar and caffeine sandwiches washed down with Coca-Cola. She thinks she'll die on a horse. I have a black and white photo of her from childhood over my desk. She is jumping a raised double gravestone. The horse and the line of a tree cast the shadow of a cross on the marble. When we are children she is always doing one dangerous thing after another with the horses, and I must follow. Sometimes I follow with my eyes shut and my ears clamped tight against the sound of disaster. We jump fire. We jump a barbed wire fence.

– I can't, I say.

– Don't say you can't. You can.

I do. Propelled by an elder sister's ferocity I can do anything. Yvonne wears Christmas beetles hooked through wire in her ears. Her garden when she is grown, when she is mother, night sister Mears, writer and artist, is full of the surprises of unfinished sculptures. She takes you around to the shed to show you a battalion of small wooden horses she's been tapping out of camphorlaurel with a chisel. Often she canters instead of walking. Exhaustion lines hang from her eyes. Over the last few years she has bought all of us black thoroughbred mares, full sisters to each other. Her children jump their bikes and fend for themselves. She owns about a hundred chickens and ducks and her garden is caged against them. They are like ballroom dancers, I say, the way they spread out across her paddocks.

– No Gillian, she says, I prefer to think they're the last of the dinosaurs. And urges me to look closely at their eyes and legs.

Her crow makes a noise.

– Don't you love that swallowed cry! I can't write about Yvonne without using exclamation marks.

Sister stories hold a kind of endlessness. They are full of surprises, even now the most familiar ones can cast up something new. We were watching you from Mum's bedroom, Karin told me a little while ago. That's how we knew where you'd buried those dead mice.

Before we went to England we ate our breakfast on the Fallen Tree at the edge of Mr Greenwood's farm, Goonelebah, near Lismore. It's a clear childhood memory. It's the house our parents build after migrating from Africa and they call the rim of the blue Dividing Range the Chimanimanis, as if they still live in Rhodesia. At the Fallen Tree our porridge is cold. We are small. Our father's mother in England, the one who was mad and sick, has died: Betty. Our mother, who Betty refused to believe existed, is singing. *Four little ducks went out one day, over the hill and faraway.* This song makes me forlorn, as if we will be separated from our mother forever. She points out to us that English rabbits in blue and crimson coats hop around and around the edges of our bowls. We're concentrating on the melted brown sugar and on walking as we eat, up and down, up and down, the long tree, stretched like a dead grey giant across the paddock. Every now and then our tongues find a small circle of hard sugar. We look for foxgloves: expecting England in Australia and never finding it. Our mother's singing voice is pale. *Oh the buzzing of the bees and the cigarette trees.* Her dress too, that morning down at the Fallen Tree, is some vague colour, a bit like the mist in my memory, rising from the small valley way beyond the boundaries of our parents' land.

We walk up and down, up and down the Fallen Tree each morning until our parents decide to remove us from school and take us with them to England for as long as it takes to sort out Betty's estate. Our father burns bonfires of old mail and ships crates full of things away to auction. We stay half a year and when we come back realise there's no disguising our difference now.

Australia seems too yellow, Honey, says our mother.
And it is.
Honeybun, says our father back. He has no remedies.
It's 1973.
We've moved from Goonelebah to Grafton and it's on every map of the world we ever look at. We even find it on the old shower curtain of the ferryman's house our parents end up buying because, though it's ugly and frail with various rots, it is on the river and the river is to entertain us in the teenage years that lie ahead, that our mother speaks of with a certain hush in her voice.
– There. Grafton, in neat helvetica type, says Yvonne, scraping away a blossom of mould with her thumb.
It's a game we continue to play for years, finding Grafton in neglected shop fronts of Ireland or on a tablecloth in Malawi. A doona cover in Fitzroy, Melbourne.
There is too much yellow in the glare coming through all the new green growth. The new town is flat and in October is said to turn mauve. Our mother spends much time trying to straighten her fine black curls with hot rollers. She's singing along to old Joan Baez and Dory Previn songs. She wears dark blue silk blouses. We are always longing to lean forward. To push the button near her breasts back through its silk slit.
– They're as narrow as nails, she likes to say about real Graftonians.
We refuse to have haircuts. Mopheads, our mother calls us. The bits of hair we never brush up on top of our heads bleach yellow too. We all get horses. Our messiness, our horsiness, betray her. To an extent she begins to abandon us and we

barely notice. She tells the same unhappy stories of her own childhood until we stop listening.

When does our mother begin to drink and have affairs? Now. The seventies, the vague years, when she favoured long and ugly evening dresses, wooden beads, beige coloured pantsuits, leather belts with embossed vines and buckles. Later she says it was the horses; the horses and her daughters who made her so careless and sad. But she was sad before Grafton, she was sad before we were born, you can see it in any old photograph. You can see it in the photographs from the Catholic orphanage her mother put her in when she was three years old and where she was left, even when the war was long over, as her father took years to die from multiple sclerosis in a monastery in Yorkshire.

Yvonne can do anything and I am her slave. I fetch and carry and obey her every order no matter how dangerous. Sonya and Karin form a counter alliance and our fights are scattered but steady. Yvonne collects china horses, Sonya and Karin china dogs. Sonya bites into two my most precious potshard stolen from the Parthenon in my sling. The kittens get put into an esky and are forgotten. No, that's not true. That story is about somebody else's little sister, but it fits. My sisters and I have left scars on each other's bodies that will be with us when we die. That wiggle of white skin next to Karin's eye when Yvonne went charging at her too wildly with a long stick. Sonya's two bottom teeth – brown and shrunken after the day I pushed her down the stairs. Though in a fit of remorse I tried to hurl myself down afterwards, my teeth remain intact.

There seems to be nothing to do at first in Grafton except injure ourselves or other things. The heat makes us scream. We have screaming contests in the bathroom where the acoustics are good and my screams always win.

Sonya and Karin, the dog-girls, drown fleas. Yvonne and I stoop to defleaing Rolf and Bella too. The guinea pigs are eaten by the dog next door. We watch flea legs flail in time to our mother's fast piano records. Each sister employs different methods of drowning and each thinks the other's less efficient. The fleas Yvonne drowns in a glass flask look like they're dancing and cast blue drowning shadows at the bottom of the water jug. We form theories as to why some fleas sink without more than one or two kicks of their legs whereas others last all day, through symphonies and suites. I'm so skinny I'm sure I've accidentally eaten flea eggs left under my fingernails and that inside me is a labyrinth of parasites. I begin to have oil in my hair and my underarms start to sweat. When our father invites some children around to our place to play we make them eat peppercorns, fleas and tadpoles before attacking them from behind with green lemons. We make the son of a soybean scientist, who is now a banker in New York, who later shaved his eyebrows into strange shapes and kissed Karin at the drive-in, howl. Hold him down, you Zulu warriors, hold him down, you Zulu chief, chief, chief, chief. We tie him up with our elastics and stomp around on top of him. Does he ever go near the water trough in our horse paddock when our father suggests his pony stay in our paddock? It's Yvonne's idea that we leave him messages. We write them on bits of old fibro. The messages are mean and mince no words. We prop them at the water trough. It's as if our sisterliness is so intense it can brook no interlopers.

The messages are signs of our malevolence, our mother says, when somehow she finds us out – and blames Yvonne. She blames Yvonne for everything, even her pain, when she is dying and Yvonne is tending to her medically in as tender a way as she knows how.

When we begin to get weekend jobs, I find there is nothing quite as forlorn as a sister in uniform, trapped and restrained and unable to act normally as I go by. I have to turn my face from Karin in the hot bread shop, Yvonne sewing bridles on a stool in the saddler, Sonya at a Woolworths checkout or my own reflection in yellow polyester uniform, making hamburgers and chips for long distance truck drivers.

Sometimes we hear rumours of Mears Girls. They arrive via Eileen Challacombe, who tells us more stories than she ever sweeps, who's always discovering various bits of pornography round our beds, who remembers how on the second time she came to our place, our mother was about to smash a plate on the kitchen floor. How our mother told her to pay no attention, it was just something she had to do. We barricade our rooms with string and notes imploring her not to enter the messy zone and usually she obeys.

Eileen looks after us while our mother is away and the rumours increase. By then we're older. The woman who owns the richest frock shop in town claims she's seen all four Mears girls copulating on her lawns. We were so drugged, this rumour went, we looked as if we were flying. In retaliation we took our horses out after dark and galloped up and down her turf. Our father made us go back the next day with sackfuls of soil from our own levee bank to fill in the holes. The letters to our mother read with a high strain of worry barely hidden beneath news of school, horses, the dirty washing getting beyond a joke and pictures of the dogs.

Some rumours begin even before we are born. The nurses can't believe we aren't all going to come out with black curls and skin because our parents, though white, are known to have arrived from Africa.

Our mother comes home and has a hysterectomy and, although we see her lying as if dead before she's through the anaesthetic, she is walking the next day.

– I'm a Mears, she says. Mears Girls don't feel pain.

These images and memories. There are so many. They are like a sad face on my wall I want to make laugh. I can feel them sometimes in my dreams, poking towards me like wishbones that haven't yet been snapped.

Our parents drink more. Memories of the Miller Street house recur because they were the unhappier times. Remembering can overwhelm us with distaste. The parties are wilder. The uncertain violence of drunk grownups. Distaste against our parents whose fault it is. Our parents barricade the rooms around their bedroom, around their weekend hangovers, but Sonya knows a route in, through two windows that won't lock, in order to thump at their door and demand a hug.

– They'd send me out to buy the *Sun Herald*, Sonya remembers. And I'd only go because I'd get icecream money as well. Even now, she says, the smell of Sunday paper cartoons can make her feel ill.

The lipstick our mother wears in Miller Street has silk powder in it so that it lasts on the lip longer. She seems afraid not to have it on when she goes out of the house but it makes her teeth look yellow near the gums. Her stomach ulcers bleed. Her nails are red. Kissed tissues float out from the top of waste paper baskets all round the house.

Sonya wears Elizabeth Arden lip-gloss and stops being with us at school. She won't ride with us to school anymore and her betrayal is keenly felt. Yvonne and I read her diary to gather an inkling of what it is all about. Sex. Then Karin too. She begins to kiss the boy we once tied up, who is shaving his eyebrows. Yvonne and I reavow our anti-marriage sentiments. We sell our geldings and buy mares. Summer, or it's warming up anyway and outside our window we can smell the Yesterday, Today and Tomorrow trees that our mother hates, but never gets around to removing, turning from white to purple.

We bring monstera deliciosa fruits into our room, eating them so fast our tongues fill with spikes as fine as stings. Under the big brooding leaves of the monstera plants I pray that I will stop blushing. My white mice die and no sister talks to me for ten or fifteen days. They go around with scalpels in their hands, dispatching certain mice of the right wild colour for their skins. Yvonne looks for ways to dye the shrivelled hides and I'm not allowed to help. White mice are pets. My sisters' white mice crawl up and down their bodies and poop in their shirts. They only kill wild mice for leather. Mouse skins tanned in this way are as soft and pale as chamois.

We skip many days of school and our mother always writes good notes. The cakes for after school turn from sponges into frozen oblongs of health cakes that are flat and dense and airless and have barely any sugar apart from a few dates thrown in. I sell a horse and over one summer spend all the money on sweets for myself and my sisters.

Before the ferryman's house in Miller Street was put on pylons the floods used to go through it. The walls when we press our faces into them smell of silt and ribbon weed. When it rains we write our animals' names in the grey mildew that grows on the fibro. I've called my mare Betty after my mad grandma whose photo is never on our father's desk or anywhere else, not even after she's dead and her wealth and belongings are all through the house.

The shapes of my sisters obsess me. I would prefer any one of their bodies to my own. I make my sisters cold, filling a bucket with iced water before creeping into the bathroom, which is ugly with fake gold trimmings, climbing onto the bath and pouring the water onto them in the shower. They scream. Their nipples curl up.

At night Karin comes into my bed following our secret signal of scratches on the dividing wall and we draw on each other's back maps of where we would like to go. She has a large globe from Hamleys toyshop on her desk and is much better at geography than I will ever be. Karin is the least horsy sister but can give the best horsebites.

Karin's travelling name is Mexican Marigold and I am Nipsy Beetle. She calls the main vein along my left arm Women River, after a river she has noticed in Canada and if her fingers are travelling along that, we are in a boat. Sometimes we take a torch with us under the blankets the better to see our destinations. She horsebites with surprise and they leave marks. If it is summer we turn my pillow over and over, seeking for anything cool. Our mother says she is going to run away to Russia so we never travel to any of the Russian cities with their lovely, icy-sounding names. There is also the game of the Red Trail which involves a more delicate kind of pain.

On wet days, Yvonne cleans our dead grandma's girlhood saddle. I hover around, ready to be helpful if necessary. I fetch her coffee sugar in a cup and her favourite teaspoon. She allows me to have every second teaspoonful. We promise each other that we will never get married. The English pigskin is as dark as the eggplants our mother's growing in the garden, trying to bring back the holiday in Greece in all the moussakas she's making. The dolmades she composes with the grapevines from the verandah don't work very well but we eat them anyway. We are growing girls. After school we eat two loaves of bread and nearly a tin of plum jam. When Yvonne puts on fresh yellow saddlesoap the pores of leather turn white. I love milk but have stopped drinking it a long time ago so that Yvonne won't smell it on my breath. We eat our cereal, porridge and Milo powder dry. The Inter Dominion is the name of a trotting heat we can hear floating to us in the evenings of the show. In Her Dominion, I think it's called. I think this for years.

We all want to know how Betty had been mad but the silences ring out from her name. Travelling around Europe and England in the back of a van, we play Madness every day. We dress up in our father's jumpers and stuff ourselves full of cushions and fruit until we take on the right proportions of a fat mad grandma.

Her past arrives into our Australian life, one afternoon, in two silver Selby's removalist trucks. The old oak furniture glints with silver and beads and old paintings lurch out of their frames. Many things are broken in the badly packed inheritance from England and all the ring drawers have been robbed. We put our fingers into the empty velvet spaces. Our mother is furious at the lack of care but doesn't mind about the rings. She has never worn rings. And none of us do or have. The smell of Goddard's silver polish enters the house. Suddenly there is silver everywhere. Our father wants us all to eat with the cutlery of his childhood, which is heavy and so large Sonya can't get the pudding spoon into her mouth. Having come from a servanted childhood, cleaning heirlooms doesn't occur to him. Somehow the arrival of all this silver in the house adds to our mother's sadness. She goes to great lengths to keep it gleaming and hides many of the more valuable pieces (she looks up identification of the hallmarks of these in fat silver textbooks she orders from Sydney) in strange places. One day Sonya finds a bundle of fish forks underneath her mattress. Our mother keeps a long pair of sixteenth-century duelling pistols, registered annually as firearms, in the sewing drawer next to the damaged pinwheels we made her in Infants.

We're paid twenty cents per half hour to help with the silver cleaning. Our fingers go pink and dry with Goddard's products.

On rainy days Sonya and I get out Betty's leather travelling bag with its many secret compartments, silver hairbrushes and half-used glass bottles of perfumes and powders. In the silk lining we find a picture of an old woman in a hat, the powder so thick on her face there is an impression that it is cracking. The face looks like one of Yvonne's earlier monsters. We regret deeply the day our father sells the case to buy Yvonne a new horse; and are kind of relieved, for we'd begun to call it the Madness Case.

Then we all leave home one after the other, fast and doing silly things; and when we return not only does the big square ugly house no longer belong to us, but it's no longer there. Late one evening I go to see the empty block with Sonya. It's been raining. The puddles in the place where our rooms and our noisiness had been are purple and soft. I have to hold back my tears.

– I'm sorry, says Sonya. As if she's responsible. It is as if that particular past has vanished and there has never been the comfort of sisterly hands.

Yet we always say our childhood was happy. Even though in some ways it was only ordinary with ordinary kinds of distress. It is a mixture in my memory, with the same sharp edge as acid drop two-for-one sweets sold in the Oliver Street corner shop.

From one of the never-used lookouts along Old Copman-hurst Road, the farm looks like a big seed pod, floating along a wide stretch of the Clarence River. Or if it's winter, a yellow plover's egg, bobbing up and down. When our mother's dying I sit at the lookout on my way back from town and in my mind the past keeps coming out as the present. Sometimes I wish, as I sit there, that I could dilute the love my sisters have always directed my way because one day they're going to find out things about me I'd rather have hidden. Somehow all the secrets will be dislodged from my guarding heart. To my sisters, who are mothers and have been for seven years, the secrets will sound outlandish. And they will bring to mind the same sense of disappointment a brown egg which turns out to be a floater can cause. Something very wholesome-looking and smooth but certainly damaged inside.

As I sit there thinking about this one overcast day at the lookout I begin to drink my mother's morphine, which is the sort of thing I mean. The thought of my sisters stops me. I only have a few sips and my mouth goes dry and pink. I hold the flask up to my eye instead so that the farm suddenly reminds me of an egg with the yolk blown out and dyed pink for Easter. I have a shameful memory of the white mice I starved to death by neglect and of how in Sonya's outstretched palm they looked like ornamental meringues for a party. Or when I dropped them into their shallow graves – gardenias in a soil the colour of a wedding cake. I think of how I didn't have my baby the year my sisters all fell pregnant.

Our mother begins to die in earnest. Yvonne and Karin travel down again and are home when the big storm of the year hits the hill. The muteness imposed by our mother lies like some soft and heavy and not all tender or pleasant thing between us. The house is full of moths. Our mother calls them death moths. They're ugly, fat and seem blind. The other day one flew out at her and she fell over. She thought it was a mouse. Wedge wings, I call them. Murder moths, says one of Yvonne's children. Killerheads. No, says Sonya, they are in fact sphinx moths. They rest up in the corners of the old furniture and are the same dark colour.

– Moths in our house mean death, says our mother, in a way I can't forget. Oh, don't look at the moon through glass, it is very bad luck, darlings.

Sadness, I think. Salt water growing more salt water crystals. Remembering the city of beautiful chemicals Sonya, Karin and I once built with Yvonne's chemistry set while Yvonne nearly blew her hand off in a homemade explosion.

Each night, whoever is in the house bandages our mother up in a configuration of bandages the medical profession calls The Spike. As we commence this procedure, carried out in the forlorn hope that it will halt the swell of our mother's body, I make sure to turn away from her face. I try to turn down Gillian Fischer singing Purcell's 'When I am Laid in Earth', that is being played on ABC FM, but my mother says to leave it. Remember me. We cry all over her. Her skin is silk – we have to massage. Everywhere, all over, feeling for the knots of small lymph nodes and moving our fingers in a clockwise or anti-clockwise direction, according to charts. I far prefer doing this with a sister than my father.

It grows dark and windows turn into mirrors. In the windows I sometimes catch sight of how we're leant over the poor beleaguered body on the massage table as if over a bier. Our mother lies with her face turned towards the river in the hope of seeing flocks of evening egrets flying from the trees. Egrets grow long filamentous plumes that were once in great demand for ladies' hats. Plumes were collected from egrets killed at their nesting colonies across the river from this house, as the feathers are best when the eggs are being laid. Yet we don't like to tell our mother that her chosen symbol of light and health has such a bloody local history.

For Yvonne, who is a nurse, who has seen such things before, it is hardest. She says she has seen women reach the size of 44-gallon drums.

I see her bending into the fire to warm the circle of massage cream in her hands. Her knuckles burn.

– That storm's coming fast! says Sonya.

– Is it wearing a halo? asks our mother.

Sonya's eyes meet mine. She is twenty-five and full of secrets and I can remember being just like that. When she tells a lie, her eyelashes flutter to the left and her head tosses in the same direction.

I think of sisterly love as being very pure and flowing. If it had a colour, it would be the kind of blue moving out from one of Yvonne's finest paintbrushes into a jar of rainwater.

– When I used to breastfeed, our mother says, the milk coming through was like silk threading out of my body.

Since the chemicals took away her hair our mother wears silk scarves theatrically, tied to give a long wild tail down her back. We look with fear and pleasure at the hair growing back like a little dark cap.

Karin begins to light all the candles in the house. One candle in a gin bottle by a window melts and is blown into the shape of a schoolgirl or an old woman with her legs pushed back at the knees. From one angle she stands the way Yvonne, trying to bow her legs into the appropriate horseriding shape long before she ever had a horse, used to stand. But from the side, the waxen head is cricked forward in a despondent way. Its belly is a poddy kind which could belong either to a girl or her grandmother.

– That's what I look like, says our mother. A little wax crone. A pregnant pygmy. Did you know the Shona buried their tiny children in wet soil but older children under rocks in the hills. I wonder will it be a wet or a sunny day for me? Yvonne! Don't put the dryer on unless you've removed the lint first or the house might burn down.

Our mother has fallen asleep in the chair where she winds her bandages. Her arm stays in the air for some time. When Yvonne goes to take the bandage away our mother wakes up.

– I'm happy doing them myself, darling, she says. You go and talk to your sisters. Within a few minutes she is asleep again, the bandage rolling to the ground this time.

I'm trying so hard to describe my sisters I think I'm failing.

They love me in such a way they fall in love sometimes with the same women I do. They fall in love with my stories of them. They write to my lover and look towards mythical times when we can all spend more time in each other's company. I fall in love with women who are better storytellers than Mears girls.

I find Yvonne looking at the black and white photograph of H rowing, which I've stuck with superglue to my desk next to the shadow of Karin.

– She has beautiful eyebrows, says Yvonne. Just like in this piece of Isak Dinesen I'm reading, her small face, with its grandly swung eyebrows . . . I'd like to try a painting.

My sister can see the same things I see in the delicate and ageing face on my desk. The same mix of age and beauty touches Yvonne as it touches me. We allow our eyes to meet and glance away.

– Do you want to come for a walk to the mail? I ask.

– No. No. I think it really has reached the stage where she shouldn't be left alone. We look away from each other again and then in the direction of our mother's bedroom, as if the walls may become transparent to our gaze.

– I think I could do anything and my sisters wouldn't mind, I tell H.

Except disappear from their lives. Vanish.

As I'm approaching the letter box I hear the mailvan and take a cartoon-like leap behind the lantana. I watch the silver ribbons of Double Swamp Creek and its silver sand. I kill hopper ants as I wait. There is the teak tree. We used to paint the seedcases silver and gold and hang them in the she-oak trees at Christmas. Inside the seedcases are the seeds. Thrown into the wind they fly away like little fawn moths. The mailman goes away. Karin too, I've heard via Sonya, has become reclusive: taking off for the gully with her children until the sound of the visitor's car has gone away again. Perhaps reclusiveness is a kind of madness and the exclusive love we reserve for sisters part of that. I begin to fear Karin and I are social phobics. When we speak to other people, we confide, the pulse in our necks hammers so much it hurts. A telephone call from a stranger will leave me drenched in sweat. We talk in a quieter and quieter way. People have to say *What?!* They must lean in towards our faces.

There's a letter from Yvonne at the bottom of the bundle. Mail is always slow from the outer Brisbane suburb where she lives. The envelope's dirty. I keep leaving the track, bumping into trees, concentrating to make out the words, for although Yvonne is only ten minutes away, her letter is full of things it is hard to talk openly about. In between writing to me, her

30

letter details, she's been sharpening knives, and one has just lopped the top off her thumb. Hence the blood. She quotes a few appropriate lines from a Plath poem and urges me to notice how her blood has fallen in diamond shapes onto my letter, describing its colour as well as foretelling that by the time it reaches me it will look like rust.

– You're right, I say to Yvonne, who's still sitting at my desk. Your blood did go like rust.

But we don't talk about what else is in the letter. I look at the sad rowing face of H but can't summon any kind of reality until glancing at Yvonne's face from this height, I suddenly know again, exactly how it would feel to put my lips onto the bone above H's eye. Have I always fallen in love with women who resemble a sister? And if so is this a bad thing? I want to write about my sisters but it is becoming very difficult.

I remember a boyfriend who travelled with a crayon self portrait and hung it in my room for awhile.

– He hasn't enough room between his mouth and his nose, Yvonne points out one day. And his fate's sealed.

Some would say we are very childish. We laugh like children, our glands of childhood keeping the pitch high. Or someone might say I have never separated sufficiently from my sisters, in a clinical sense, and they would be right. So that we feel silent except in their company, having in a way been robbed of a normal language.

– Is this also H? asks Yvonne, still looking at my noticeboard.

– No, that's Karin's shadow.

Seventeen days after my birthday, our mother's abdomen is drained at the local hospital and her phony pregnancy falls away from her. She seems to disappear in bed and for the first time in her life, doesn't get up. The next day and Yvonne and Karin drive down again. My mother thinks the burble of their V8 engines is a jumbo jet flying overhead.

– I'll always be like another sister, won't I? She says with her hand in my hair.

These are her last words for me. She dies early in the morning. My ears seem to grow cold, as if they are being cried on. Our mother's face looks Byzantine and slightly mauve. At the moment, I still cannot look at photographs of Yvonne, Karin or Sonya upside down due to the impression this gives of somebody having taken photographs of my sisters after death.

There is a Tear Tree in Africa, I remember our mother telling us once, or perhaps it was on the Canary Islands, she is dead now and I cannot ever check the facts again, that cries for a week during the hot dry days just before the summer rains. The ground below such trees becomes saturated. The tree tears are large and rolling. This is how we cry, I think. And we cry with hardly any noise wishing our father wouldn't.

The mist is being ripped apart by sun as we walk away up the farm hill and look, look says Sonya, don't the early morning egrets look like tissue paper floating over the river? It is the first time I've ever held Sonya's hand, as opposed to shaken and squeezed it and I'm aware how delicate it is. Even when I was in the labour ward with her when BB her last son was born, she bit her own arm and didn't take my hand.

Later, when the funeral director comes, we all creep to other parts of the house. I watch from the water tank. The stretcher is green and there is the funeral director who is rumoured to drink gin lemonades each evening until he passes out.

Sonya spends the day dyeing all our mother's cashmere jumpers black. The cotton darns do not absorb the black pigment. In the laundry sink the jumpers look like drowned grey babies. She cries as she pokes at the jumpers still at the simmer on the stove. She walks from stove to sink and back again. Her crying sounds like a bird in danger that I don't know how to save.

Somebody takes a photo of us. My hand over Sonya's

shoulder looks dead. As if somebody took it off at the wrist and hung it on a sister to drain.

Outside the cathedral is our mother's old car that she sold many years before. The cathedral is full, though only two or three people who were not daughters were allowed to visit her once she was sick. I look inside the car remembering the family dog Rolf as he looked laid out on a picnic rug after being hit by a car. The fleas were still alive. I kept wondering, as he was buried, are fleas on a dead dog like rats on a sinking ship? Would they know to get off before the earth began to go on? Our mother planted strawberries over Rolf, which were always eaten before they were ripe by other scavenging sisters.

Eileen deliberately misreads the reading:

. . . she brings home food from out of the way places, as merchant ships do. She gets up before daylight to prepare food for her family and to tell her servant girl what to do . . .

Servant girl not servant girls as really reads in the Bible. A small pun for us. A small pun from Eileen to make us smile through the crying.

In the church I see how the hairs on Yvonne's legs curl back under the black stockings Sonya lent her and that there are fissures and cracks in the heels of her feet. By the time we reach Copmanhurst cemetery the stockings have laddered on the skin of my sister's feet. Our mother would say dab a bit of nailpolish on, don't throw them out. I can hear her voice. She was frugal and extravagant both at once.

The hole that has been dug, says the funeral director, is big enough to fit a Volkswagen. We carry the coffin again and again I am too tall – unbalancing the rest of the sisters.

We all cry with only our left eyes, so that the gathering of people on the other side of us don't see our tears. I suppose this is peculiar.

– I want to be buried in a sheet, says Karin when it's just us left by the grave. Let the worms get to their work fast.

– Me too, says Sonya.

– Wrap me up in my stockwhip and blanket, says Yvonne.

– You can pop me in a crochet rug. We're really weeping now, both eyes, as well as laughing.

– Don't all just disappear at the farm, will you? says our father. I want you girls to talk to people.

We all disappear.

I dream my sisters die and wake up in sheets drowned in tears. It is the same when reading about the death of Janet Frame's sisters. And on a train journey to Sydney I hear two old sisters talking about the death of their youngest sister.

– Who'd ever have thought, they say to each other, that Eily would be the one to make the first break. They unwrap small squares of fruitcake to eat, oblivious to the tears slipping unhankied from my eyes. I can imagine nothing more painful than the death of one of my sisters and hold onto the selfish hope that like Eily, I will make the first break. This, it turns out, is also the wish of Yvonne, Karin and Sonya. Our mother died young and she was always sad. She had a sad core.

At Central there often seem to be sisters travelling to and from each other. I am sitting near an ancient little man. His wife is growling at him. 'She's just been with her sisters,' he says to me. 'Been visiting them in turn. She always gets like this afterwards. She'll settle down after awhile.'

It's as if nothing can quite match sisterly love. Maybe we hold irrationally tight to its sensations. Perhaps forever. We can't believe our mother has died. We return to the scene over and again. We tell stories to each other, trying to recollect exact sequences of events.

– I'm a Mears Girl, aren't I? says one of the nephews, sitting with his school shoes up against the kitchen counter. 'The Pale Dark', by Hampster Mears, he writes at the top of his picture while eating all the soft centres out of the chocolates our mother has given him to share out.

I have often written about sisters. Whenever writing about these fictional sisters I've found myself battling a sense of phoniness. I continue to wait for someone to point out to me that something is not quite right with the point of view of my sisters. What exactly do I mean? I mean I've always invented Australian voices for them, with retinues of Australian aunts, uncles, friends and grandmothers to prop up their voices. When in fact, the reality was only us. Only Yvonne, Karin, Gillian and Sonya. Take the first letter of each of my sisters, reverse the age order and you can spell the sky. I think of sisterly love as being blue and light or dark and sad, plumbago or plum-coloured, prone to change, affected by weather and mood. And shifts of alliance always rearranging the patterns that bind us. Sequins of shade and light seem to be dancing towards me from the leaves of the old Port Jackson fig. Thinking about sisters can make my sentences seem too tender.

It's dark under that tree. As the paraphernalia of death begins to surround our mother I go out into the garden and open my mouth under the tree to swallow in the cool and thick sensations. Yvonne pushes off a dog and sits in the giant grey padded recliner from the cancer clinic, which Sonya calls the throne. The tickbirds in the willows by the river made those trees look exotic and sad, like magnolia trees. The dark makes me feel like crying. Karin finds the first freesia and we take it in turns, dipping our long noses towards the flower that will accompany our mother to her death. Words desert us. A coolness floats from the flower in a way reminiscent of hanging wet, clean washing in a wind, or putting your face close up to dry ice.

We keep a fire going, so big the grate explodes.

We remember our mother loved fires. She would go out into the cold. I am looking for knubbly bits, she would say. She used to dry lines of wishbones for us above the fire in order that they would snap fairly. In order not to mix chicken grease and wishes. The delicate snap! Sonya used to suck the marrow out of bones. It is the day before Christmas when the ultrasound technician can't conceal his horror in front of our mother's gaze at what he sees in her liver and lungs, but that night she decorates the cake, apologising that the cake is so thin. Confessing that she has been taking off slivers from the bottom since it was made. Taking care not to disturb her icing.

Sonya thinks she will die by a blood vessel in her brain becoming so frail it bursts. Or maybe, she says, it will be a big crash from one of the racehorses she speeds around the Grafton racetrack on, in the near dark each morning. Asthma.

Karin thinks a shark is going to eat her and no longer swims in the sea or the river. Or that she has a slushy pulse and that will be her end.

– Have a feel, have a feel, she will urge, placing your fingers to her neck so you can feel the slur of blood that is due to a damaged valve.

Yvonne looks me straight in the eye and says for her it will be a horse accident. She wants nothing less than a dramatic death.

Only when we die will our childhood gland also disappear. According to Karin's university notes the thymus, the gland of childhood, should shrivel and vanish by the time you are sixteen. It is the gland that keeps a child a child. I think we'd find ours still, in under our hearts and fatter than ever.

I write to Karin to tell her of my recurring image of her sitting in the rusting chair in the middle of her circular rosebed. In this image her baby is strapped to the front of her body and she holds a hose towards rose bushes afloat with old blossoms. Past the roses are yellow and green paddocks and beyond them the blue edges of Scenic Rim, so vague with mist they could be painted there in sunfaded watercolours. The baby Sonya sleeps with a mouth like a slightly open rosebud between my sister's breasts.

Karin writes back the same day on the back of an envelope. The grass has grown so high she would disappear if she sat down and only two rose flowers, like white faces, poke out at her over the jungle of grass and castor oil bushes.

– I AM a Mears Girl, says the same nephew, still sitting with his school shoes up against the kitchen counter. Sonya? he asks.

Sometimes I think I know everything there is to know about my sisters but this isn't true. I talk about them too much to strangers and worry afterwards that I've left out everything that is important.

Like the shadows on a sister's neck from an earring. Moving as she laughs. Look! I want to say. I have always wanted people to see everything that is beautiful about them. For the ordinary to be transformed. See their necks so long and swannish when they tip back their heads to laugh. The Mears crest is four English swans. There on all the old cutlery and seals.

And the way they make their children laugh.

How Yvonne urges me to tell my stories sideways. Her mind going at a hand gallop to my steady pace. And she would tell everything differently, faster, with a blare. All my sisters would and there would be different stories, and other memories, less defined, incomplete, mysterious to me – of our child-hood – where figures and events keep slipping in and out of focus. Such movement.

See, I want to say.

HOUSES, SISTERS, CITIES

BETH YAHP

My secret life, that eggshell shape, was as frail as icing curtains. One handsweep and all was splinters, sprinkled careless across the kitchen floor. My sister and I stooped to pick at the pieces with careful fingers. In our mouths the shards crumbled to mere sugar, and we sucked noisily, and smacked our lips. Always at birthdays we were allowed the leftover icing. On a shelf too high for childish fingers, even standing tiptoe, the birthday cakes sat waiting for evening under their fly covers, rainbow cakes clustered with delicate roses, pineapple upside-down cakes with imported cherries and trails of silver beads. Squares of cut paper held the failed roses too watery to keep their shape. The icing powdered the backs of our hands. How deft the squeeze needed to curl the petals just so, to droop their edges to a raggedy semblance of realness, how precise the flick of the wrist. Giving up on roses we made rows of smile shapes instead, determined half-circles, brocaded, like Indian lace on the hems of birthday dresses. One layer overlapping another. Like the red ruched curtains at the local cinema before the sudden dark. My sister and I twisted ourselves into those heavy curtains, we pressed our faces to them, tangled arms and legs in spins and squeals to bring the usher running. The icing curtains we couldn't press our faces to. They dried hard and brittle on their strips of cake paper, not the heavy red of cinema smells and chairs creaking, but in little girl shades of pink and cream. Held to the light their weight crinkled the paper, they lightened from opaque to milky, to see-through swirls.

* * *

When I think of my sister it is the shape of our hands I think of, and our wrists and ankles, and the houses we lived in, the foods we ate, our night-time talk and thunderstorm stories, the clothes we used to wear. Our various haircuts over the years. I remember these in old black and white photos, and ones in which the colours are fading; in the wide swing of black-papered albums opened on tropical evenings, and not every so often either, and only far away. The houses I remember are more the parts of houses, bedrooms and kitchens, porches, gardens, certain windows: the vague geography of memory, with dusty unpacked cartons under the stairs. In those days my father was a travelling salesman. He filled our childhood with different-shaped houses, wrong-way-round corridors, steps that sent us tumbling in the weeks before our feet learnt their routine. The different-shaped rooms confused the long minutes before sleep: our eyes open to yet another unfamiliar dark. My mother knelt at our bedside with arms crossed over her breasts and words to keep the dark at bay. *As I lay me down to sleep, I pray the Lord my soul to keep. If I should die before I wake, I pray the Lord my soul to take.* Smoke from the mosquito coil shivered as she shooed demons out from under the bed. She twitched the newly-hung curtains over the new neighbours' voices, and their midnight feuds and curries, and lamplit movements scaring shadows into our room. She left a whisper of English lavender behind her and sometimes the lacy edge of her nightgown caught in the door.

In those days my father filled our childhood with his absence. Those days and even years later, from eight till six every weekday, and half-days on Saturdays with a night's entertaining to follow, and only Sundays, after church, completely free. The suitcase on the bed, half-packed or unpacked, was a usual sight. The car groaning out of the driveway, his arm waving at right angles, his outstation phone calls rushed by the neighbour's child like a gift to our window.

My mother's sudden smiling announcement, *Girls, your father's coming home.* My mother in those days was a mother of sleeveless blouses and talcum powder, of full cream milk and boiled eggs in the mornings, a proper breakfast, and rosewater left over from the days she was a young missy of the house. Her sisters, one unmarried, the other widowed, one saintly, the other temperamental, sent her good quality presents wrapped in thick patterned paper once a year. The lengths of cloth were stiff, sometimes pinned with the name of a good Singapore tailor. Cakes of lavender soap lined the bathroom shelf. My mother's sisters sent her the Mrs Beaton's cookbook she learnt to cook from in their kitchen, and copperplate advice on married life. Once a bottle of holy water from Lourdes that flaked its corked cover into itself when shaken over the years. A brown drizzle at first, then a snowstorm. My sister and I stood tiptoe reaching for this bottle. Even at an early age we understood the dangers involved in reaching for magic of any kind. We looked over our shoulders to make sure the doorway was empty. We climbed a haphazard mountain of chairs.

In fact the new neighbours' lights were fluorescent and cast a hard white light through the newly-hung curtain cracks into our room. My sister and I lay breathing the last of the lavender. So soon that smell of my mother, faintly milky, mixed with flowers we had never seen and years later would stop to stare at in foreign gardens, and crumble between our fingers, even then disbelieving their undried stalks, their sap, soon her smell disappeared into the dark. That hot tropical dark of a satellite city, grey at best, never truly night. Air you could swim in. My sister and I crept from our bed to pull at the curtains as though parting a stage. No one who has not walked in a tropical city can imagine this air. Filled with ribbons of sound and smell swollen moist and tangled so a step backwards is necessary upon meeting it. Even now we watch the sweat

43

spilling from tourists, gathering in patches on their backs and armpits, and we laugh at their unaccustomed heads boiled bright red. Ours absorb so much heat we have to snatch our hands away. My sister and I make faces at the way the air hits even us, that abandoned air, forgotten in the cooler climates we have chosen to live in, remembering us with a vengeance as we step from the plane. The first days of our visits knocked horizontal, stretched out in shorts and singlets with a fan whirling overhead.

The backstreet between our and the neighbours' row of terrace houses was like a river in the night. Nothing grew on this street, it was potholes and rubbish spilling from plastic bags. Groups of shadowy young men passed with a crunching of gravel on their way to and from the squatter village. In the lighted slabs of street they were startled into assuming recognisable shapes, bony faces lifting upwards, the peak of a baseball cap pushed back. Bolts of laughter trailed their cigarette smoke behind them, and a scuffle of footsteps once in a while. The babble of voices, comforting, as working women strolled home. My sister and I watched stray dogs picking through the pools of light from this or that bedroom or kitchen, and the gangs of squatter children edging their way around them, now a foot lit, now an elbow. We listened to the hushed sounds of scrabbling, a wire fence climbed, then a rustle of leaves and a sudden loud snap. A backdoor shouted open, the creak of the fence leapt over and footsteps now running, running. The branch of prize mangoes raced from someone's backyard off into the dark. This nightly stream we could almost reach out and touch. For what seemed like hours we stood leaning our foreheads against the barred window as the neighbours opposite danced their supper ritual of plates and glasses and chairs scraped forwards then back. Their words slipped out between sucked fingers in bursts my sister and I could almost decipher. We stood at the window until my mother returned to scold us back into bed. In the daytime we slipped into the house's hidden spaces, under stairways, stretched out between bookshelves with the books pushed out, or curled into the thunderstorm spaces under a bed. The games my sister invented took us to places long ago and faraway, from which we watched ourselves as knights and fairies, rebel kung fu fighters, French legionnaires. She was always Johnny Johnson and I Beau Geste, the cowardly killed one, we wore my father's handkerchiefs tucked into our caps. We watched lightning streak across the floor, and my mother's feet padding from the kitchen, her calls searching for us from room to room. In those days it was always *my sister and I*, though she was the one who said it, to once-in-a-while visitors and festival relatives and even strangers stopping to lean their hands through the bars of our front gate. In those days it was always *we*.

We three, said my mother, *meeting on a train. That first meeting, on the Bangkok train.* My mother's stories filled the quiet hour of completed housework, before the evening meal had to be prepared. We three sat cross-legged with our knees touching, mandala-shaped on the cool cement, with Lego blocks between us or an ark of plastic animals and my mother's head bent as low as ours, her brow as creased with concentration, her ear cupped to a game of whispers if that was the game. For a moment we were three sisters busy with our plastic cooksets, we were three yaksas guarding the tops of mountains, we were three cosy bears. During the monsoon season we huddled in the darkened house, the sound of her stories forever entangled with rain against slatted glass. Like her smell we could recognise her voice anywhere, anytime. In crowded markets when our hands slipped their anchor on her basket to plunge us into a jungle of strangers whose bustle was no longer friendly, all we had to do was stand still. My sister and I stood hand in hand, my mouth already rounding, prickles starting in the corners of my eyes, which only her fierce

45

handgrip held in check. Not long before I learnt that all we had to do was listen. Even through the market babble we could hear my mother, the pattern of her voice imprinted in our ears. We pushed towards that rising inflection, unmistakable, to find her bent over one stall or another with a vendor hovering, whispering special recipes for this or that meat or vegetable which he'd tell only her. My mother turned to smile at us as though she had noticed neither our absence nor return. She poked at the proffered flatfish or snake beans, a disdainful toss of her head and she'd moved on to another stall. All the market vendors knew her. *Missus!* they called from across the street. *Auntie, over here!* lifting goods hidden under counters especially for her. My mother bent the tips of ladies fingers and baby carrots to test their freshness, her basket filled till her arm was lined with its plaited stripes. My sister and I were allowed to carry the packets of soybean custard swirling in ginger syrup, our market-day treat, and the three kinds of meat for each of our family's favourite dish: bone and marrow soup for my father, steamed salted chicken for my sister, double-cooked pork for me.

Even laden with newspaper parcels of all shapes and sizes my mother walked so quickly we could hardly keep up. Only at the bus stop did the crowd sweep us ahead of her, we fitted into the spaces under elbows, between adult bodies, we were squashed and pummelled and lifted into the bus. My sister and I stood in the doorway, our legs straddled, hands snatching at baskets and hemlines, letting no one pass. This was our particular terror, my mother's voice in the quiet afternoon yesterday or the day before or some other day we could hardly remember except for her voice coming upon us at her dressing table with our faces daubed with powder, our heads plastered with vanishing cream. Our clothes drenched with so much rosewater we were an open bottle. *Girls, what are you up to?* that incredulous voice hurrying us to the bathroom, but almost laughing also, though her words came out stern. *Aiya, naughty*

46

girls, can't Mummy leave you alone for one minute? You'd better be good, or tomorrow I'll leave you at the market. This was our particular terror. *Be good! Or Mummy will give you to the medicine shop man.* My sister and I waited outside shops that were closing, we pushed the doors back open, poked our heads in to make sure my mother was still there. We craned around corners for other exits, the disappearing flurry of her dress. *Aiya, these girls! They're too naughty, do you want them?* As the bus pulled away from the market crowd with her struggling in it we cried *Stop!* loud and terrified enough to make the driver slam his brakes. *Stop, don't go yet! Let my Mummy in!* The crowd reluctantly parted and, smiling, my mother climbed in.

Nowadays her voice on the phone is a thread to the crush and swell of those markets; it seems fish cakes and diesel fumes make the satellite leap with her stories into my room. My sister smells them from the other side of the world. Through the window the Sydney sky becomes tropical cloudy, the London traffic remote. The afternoons of our visits home too are filled with my mother's stories, though they aren't the ones we remember; these days she speaks the plots of market gossip and American soap operas, dog-and-cat antics, marauding iguanas harried to death with sticks. She speaks bougainvillea that refuses to flower like the ones in her memory and too many bananas in their garden harvest for her and my father to eat. Once in a while she asks after one of her sisters, who lives twenty kilometres from me. On the first days of our visits my sister and I have to lean away. The flow of words is relentless, the movement of my mother's mouth all we can see, and the walls of the kitchen, the dining room, the air-conditioned bedroom where we rest after dinner echo with more words than we can take in. Her words clatter around us, and this is how we remember her, the mother of those childhood houses, towering over us, spilling stories, yet even then there were periods of black silences, with only pots and pans clanking their metallic voices and a fierce swish of the vegetable knife. *Go away, get out. Go and play*, spoken with such finality there was nothing else to do. My sister and I went with the sharp shrug of her elbow in our hands. Hours or days later, when her smile was suddenly noticed, her palm pressed to an unsuspecting forehead, her arms reaching around my father and their words murmuring from behind their locked door, once again the house could breathe. After her silence my mother's laughter was always surprising. When especially delighted she threw back her head. She had a way of exclaiming like a startled bird.

My mother first saw her sisters through the window of the train. She stood leaning her chin against the windowsill, stooping slightly, elbows propped on each side of her face. Her fingers lay against her hair like an elaborate head-dress, her back and legs stuck out at uneasy angles. She seemed all elbows and knees. In those days my mother's body was at odds with everything, with her clothes, her movements, the wooden seats of the carriage, the women and children bumping against each other to retrieve their possessions. Her flesh was at odds with her bones. Even hunched over she was almost as tall as Mamanan. No one knew how old she was. Later, citizenship forms would be filled by guessing her age from her size and height. *Eleven? No, she looks fifteen. I'd say at least fifteen.* My mother had no pieces of paper to tell her who she was. She was born the month the jackfruit tree was planted in so-and-so's garden, in the city now left behind, that she wouldn't return to until decades had passed and canals been paved over, and she no longer recognised the whole city, let alone its childhood streets. Her new sisters stood side by side on the platform, one all soft curves and expectancy, the other as thin as a rake. Their heads craned from window to window, in the surge of people they alone were still. My mother picked them out immediately. They were Eurasian, half-European, half-Asian, their hair and eyes and skin like watered silk, faded in comparison to the ones around them. The sisters stood cool and aloof amidst the station bustle, handkerchiefs pressed to their nostrils, beautiful in tailored dresses with jackets in spite of the midday heat. One had their mother's broad forehead, the other her small bony build. Both her startling, secretive expression that made people stare. The sisters reached their hands through the train window to Mamanan. Their arms brushed against my mother's shoulder. She still remembers the feel of their skin. She pulled herself back into the carriage, gathered their bags and parcels as Mamanan directed, and they jostled their way out of the train.

The secret life, that eggshell shape, who can say what are its beginnings? By the time I walk with my sister in London mine seems as craggy as the humpbacked houses lining her street. As ancient as the women bent over shopping bags in their doorways, whose tent shapes turn towards us smiles so cracked and beautiful we are surprised into smiling back. *Don't look at strangers, don't smile. Be good, or I'll give you to the madwoman. The madwoman will take you away*. What extraordinary egg stays balanced at the back of the throat for years, now gurgling forward, now receding, like styrofoam beads on the crest of a water fountain, at every moment almost gurgling away. My sister and I took turns pressing the speckled button that needed just so much pressure, no more, to swivel the beads or leaf shreds or paddle-pop pieces in a showy defiance of gravity for the half minute before the prefects came to chase us away. If we narrowed our eyes the water became invisible, the beads dancing only on sunlight and air. My sister and I ran great risks to work this magic. Only at the last moment did we skip away from the prefects with their punishment books, our movements sure and purposeful, our elbows linked, hands cradled to the giggles spurting from our mouths. We disappeared into the schoolgirl swarm. In London our walk is tentative, never bumping shoulders. We stand side by side looking in through shop windows for the perfect not-too-Chinese not-too-white wedding dress. Something in red and white. We have an afternoon to do this, my sister's schedule is so busy. We wander around the clothes racks, she walking briskly, pulling faces, me trailing behind her, pushing the rows of coathangers askew. Ours is the walk of acquaintances, polite, our histories packaged neatly inside us. No accidental leaking. In Kuala Lumpur we are surprised by sisters, as old as we are, who stroll about untidily, arm in arm.

By the time we walk in London I am taller than my sister, I am a dress size larger, my palms pressed together make a steeple whose shadow completely swallows hers. I am too large in London, my shoes are boats in her corridor, in the pictures of us together I am looming, my shoulders no longer hunched, stomach sucked in no more. My sister has my mother's fine bones and her rounded eyes. She wears the same thin shape of her late twenties. In London we tip forwards with a peck on each cheek for greeting, we say *How good to see you* and *What are you up to?* and then step back with *My, how well you look!* We talk about work and the weather, Londoners, Sydneysiders, other travellers, how my flight was, how long I'll stay. By evening we are sitting cross-legged in the kitchen, eating cornflakes and chocolate biscuits, checking our feet for the beginnings of bunions that will swell them like my mother's and make our footprints wedge-shaped paddles, instantly recognisable. We wonder about her life these days, what *does* she do in that big tropical house by herself on the long days when my father is at work or away on business, with only her garden and two rowdy dogs for company, instead of two girls. Mamanan and my aunts described my mother as a boisterous runaround girl but to us she has always seemed wary of people. In all the years of our childhood houses my sister and I remember only one friend.

In her kitchen I look through the window and the London dusk hangs as low and purple as the headache shadows under my mother's eyes and like them seems to last forever. Over her house at this time there would be a large setting moon. When the cornflakes and biscuits are finished and the talk grown scraggly my sister and I sit looking at each other, moving our feet and lacing and unlacing our fingers, murmuring *How good to be here, How good to have you here* as though there are no headache days in our memory, no secrets, no lives to speak of except for those in our childhood houses, and the ones we have made for ourselves in London and Sydney, our sudden cut-off lives: oceans apart and only occasionally strung with postcards. As though *How good* with a sigh is what we have waited all these years to say.

By the time we knew her my mother had a space inside her, hard as eggshells and just as brittle, where she kept the sharp edge of the teak sofa, and the voices rising, the looks over shoulders and lips pressed resolutely, the slamming of doors. The twisting and turning of streets leading nowhere familiar, the rattle of a train from Bangkok with its tracks shrinking to nothing no matter how hard she looked. In our childhood houses it became a forgotten space tucked amongst the unpacked cartons under the stairs. Those houses were filled with our children's voices, with running a household, arranging chairs from the thrift shop to their best advantage, dreading rent-collector Fridays when the gate was shaken and shaken, and only my sister and I dared poke out our heads. *Go away, Mister! Nobody's here!* Those were days of a young husband who drove miles to lunch with her and came home tired to wash baby clothes and help cook dinner and play trains and horsy and one-armed swordsmen with my sister and me. In the evenings my mother sat with her sewing. Her evening hands were busy with needle and buttons, worn shirts and socks or an edging of birthday lace. Her evening voice we hardly recognised, it was rounded with secret laughters, with waiting for my father to speak. My father carried the world into our livingroom, he eclipsed the afternoon stories with road accidents, crises at the office, dealers with two wives and eight children who haunted nightclubs looking for a third. His voice was as compact as the space he occupied at the dining table, or in his favourite armchair, precise, his space and no more. No room for contradiction. My mother listened with her hands flitting over cloth. She nodded and smiled, and cried out with horror or pleasure or surprise, but her hands never stopped. My sister and I were beckoned and the birthday dresses held against us while we looked from her to my father, and back. The bridge of words between them was a slippery place. My father's evening face broke like water, his smiles so sudden, his teeth so yellow and long. My mother's was beautiful to look at, her hair curled against the part of her throat that trembled when she laughed.

Later she let us drape the rows of favourite lace around our necks. Some of it, rolled into tight barrels, had come with her and Mamanan on the Bangkok train. My mother carefully arranged them in their woven basket, every now and then they were unpinned and examined to match this or that special cloth. She showed us the stitches Mamanan taught her, stem and petal stitches, knots and crosses, careless running ones for tacking, the invisible rows with which to edge fine handker-chiefs. In Bangkok Mamanan sat sewing late into the night to send my mother to school, to learn Siamese in the mornings and English in the afternoons, and spend the evenings sneaking away from homework, roaming the neighbourhood with her friends. Mamanan shouted from their front verandah, banging on a tin to call her home. A quick duck to the left as she ran into the house and Mamanan's knuckles always missed. In Bangkok my mother was dressed in her best clothes the day she went with Mamanan. Her own mother slapped the top of her head. *Do you want to go with Auntie, or not? Sit still while Mama combs your hair.* Her older sisters stood sulking as my mother followed Mamanan into the street, too excited by the prospect of a special outing to even turn and wave. Mamanan's hand was large and soft around hers, the jewellery around her neck, wrists and ankles jingled as she walked. She wore great golden droplets in her ears. *Tomorrow I'll take you home,* she told my mother, and then *Tomorrow* and *Tomorrow*, and finally *Be quiet! It's because your mother has too many useless girls. She doesn't want you! You're so naughty she gave you away. Look, she sent all your clothes.* In Bangkok my mother became an only daughter. She no longer had any sisters except for copperplate ones from Kuala Lumpur who arrived in pale blue envelopes punctually once every month.

In Kuala Lumpur Mamanan was converted by her older daughters and my mother was christened Mary. After their convent education the sisters emerged well-groomed and ladylike, one on her way to teachers' college, the other in stiff imported silk down the aisle. The sisters were known for being pious and good. After the wedding they sent for Mamanan, who insisted on bringing the girl she had adopted to fill the years of their absence. My mother of the bare feet and face streaked with any-old-how powder when chided into grooming bore too many traces of the barbarian upbringing that had made their English father pack them off to a convent in another country just before he died. The old English professor left his Siamese widow with no children, but money enough to be cheated by her numerous friends and relatives and end up a seamstress sewing her fingers to the bone. In their faraway classrooms and dormitories, amidst the routine of quiet voices, of kneeling and rising and bowing the head, the sisters remembered a mother nicknamed *My barbarian,* who was small and fiery, whose rings and bangles cut white scars into their heads and shoulders and arms. When they emerged from the convent they were more their dead father's daughters than hers. They were intent on scolding civilisation into my mother. When she stepped with Mamanan from the Bangkok train the sisters eyed her from head to toe. They directed her to the front seat next to the gloved and uniformed driver, the parcel of bottled sambals, curry pastes and pickled vegetables that Mamanan insisted on bringing from Bangkok for her daughters carefully balanced on her knees. The sisters ordered all the windows wound right down, they sat one on each side of Mamanan and one squeezed her nostrils shut with her handkerchief, her head sagging against the seat, while the other pointed out this or that landmark that my mother did not turn her head to see.

At her christening she wore a white dress specially handed down and let out for the occasion. The gauzy veil drifting onto her shoulders made her swirl her head from side to side, her lips curled with pleasure when she caught sight of her shiny white shoes. No photos survive of this event. In the ones we have my mother is older, she is surrounded by nieces and nephews who look like her brothers and sisters, she is leaning against the kitchen doorway or sitting movie-star style under a tree with her hair scraped back and the corners of her lips almost lifting. She wears billowing skirts and checked shirts with the collars turned up. Her arms are draped around a succession of dogs. She is so thin it is hard to imagine a girl outgrowing her clothes so quickly that friends and in-laws were invited to stare when she entered a room. *Mary, can't you walk quietly? Look at you! My, what a big thumping woman you will grow up to be.* Easy to imagine those knob bones and hollow cheeks caused by picking at her food in spite of waste and starving children and *you don't know how lucky you are.* By drinking a dose of vinegar three times a day. *Mary is my name,* my mother said later, in her soft afternoon voice though it was morning or evening or more often long past midnight, with her stepping out of the dark like a magician, and the house suddenly flooded with light. My sister and I stopped, caught red-handed slipping in the door. *Mary meaning bitter, standing for bitterness*, and as she said this we saw that she carried the taste of her name on her tongue.

This is the situation, then, three women in a house, though most of the time we are in those childhood houses two of us aren't yet women, we aren't anything yet but eyes widening and a flow of questions, and one day we are rushing around the house leaving toys in unexpected corners, parading in dress-ups to set the neighbours laughing, and we are standing at the gate, looking up at strangers, making faces at the local madwoman; and then we are leaving, it is hard to make us at first, we only go out a certain number of hours every day, on an errand to the shops or to school or sport or the local cinema or choir practice at church, and then we are going out and coming back, and going out, and this seems to last forever, the rhythms of coming and going, the front gate clanging, but then we are going out, and out again, and the sounds of the nights are enormous, and one of the women spends them listening, listening. The nights are filled with the sounds of motorbikes, but never the right ones, never a purring pause at the gate, then a roar away, followed by footsteps. The clink of coming-home keys. We are sitting at the dinner table remembering how we used to crash swords against each other like movie heroes and drive the usher crazy by running up and down the aisle. We're remembering the day one of us could finally reach the top of the fridge and how she turned to lift the other so she could reach it too. We are remembering scraped knees. Three women in a house. One woman, and two who have discovered narrowed eyes and books, magazines and television instead of questions. A world outside the pulled-apart curtains, the locked front gate. When one after another, too quickly, much too quickly, those two are on their way to becoming women, that is when the trouble starts.

55

The trouble with the architecture of memory is that no matter how wobbly the stairs and floorboards, how the place hangs with cobwebs and the roof leaks, and the windows are cracked and starry, it is a place we enter headlong, my mother, my sister and I. No matter how shaky the beams. Our memory is a house we enter through different doors, in which we seldom encounter each other and are always surprised that we don't. No corridors lead directly from front to back. There are closets galore. In my study, a continent away, crowded with books and papers, with only four paces from one wall to another, it seems a house too large and unwieldy. Unlike the ones in the fairytale jungles of my mother's afternoon stories our house lies in wait not for hapless wanderers, only us, although in our faraway kitchens, eating cornflakes and chocolate biscuits, we too come upon it suddenly. Like wise wanderers we have to tread carefully, my sister and I. Only certain rooms are safe for walking. Brush against an unexpected doorknob or window ledge, or even a creeper overhanging a window ledge, too rough a brush and the house will collapse, we'll have to walk a rain of bricks and mortar, with the stuff of attics thrown in.

In London it is pleasing to enter a restaurant my sister has told me about, which makes Malaysian chicken rice *just like back home*, and have the waiter pull out my chair with *How nice to see you again*. This never happens in Sydney. No one mistakes me for anyone, in Sydney I am always myself. As they used to in our childhood houses people in London can tell we are sisters by our shadows. By the way we walk, the lean of our bodies at just such an angle, the way we tilt our heads. Our energetic wave of hands. On the phone there is confusion before our accents give us away. My sister's friends stare at me in astonishment, all these years they have seen her as completely unique. Smiles meant for her curl at the corners of their lips and after a moment they are saying *Remember the time*, then stopping at my quick shake of the head. My sudden wry smile. *Twins!* others exclaim, because even our haircuts are the same, I've been given the secret of her favourite hairdresser, the only one in London who *knows about Asian hair*. In London it is easy to fall into patterns of behaviour we haven't fallen for in years. My sister walks slightly ahead of me, and this is also the way we talk. The way we plan outings and tidy the house for my parents' arrival, and make dinner, and get into the car. She is two years and two months older than me. Slightly behind, I can look at her. I can measure our wrists and ankles, set elbows against each other, our chins and foreheads and noses. Those solid measurable things. I can look at the words that trail after her *You're my sister, liking doesn't come into it*, and watch the backward kick of her legs as she takes off for an appointment for which she is late. Her energy flattens me onto her sofa after she has left, I lie with the blinds shut on London, watching videos for hours.

My sister comes home to perch on a stool in the kitchen and plan production schedules until three a.m. three days, then two, then one day before her wedding. She leaves for work at five in the morning to return only well after dark. She holds up her ring so its history can be seen. Two geckoes eating an amethyst form the band, their eyes are glints of emerald and ruby, their mouths gorging on the purple stone. There's a crack in the amethyst that is visible only by staring hard, but my sister thinks it is growing. She sends it back to the jeweller's for the stone to be changed, once, twice, and again. She tells me her original plan: the geckoes swallowing a hollow crystal filled with her fiancé's blood, dark and red on her finger. She laughs describing Marcus turning pale at the sight of the needle, a childhood phobia, and people staring at her ring, then her, then back at the ring. As she says this I watch him cup the back of her neck with his hand, plant her head with kisses. My sister absently tilts her head away. One night the crystal leaked its contents into the creases between her fingers. She waves her hands to shape her disappointment, but the amethyst looks innocent, not merely a replacement, not flawed. Her bloodied ring is something I could never have imagined, it is like the childhood games she invented, like the hats she wears, ones I would dare to wear only in stories, all odd shapes and flamboyance. Unbelievable folds. In London I watch the wave of my sister's hands. I keep my own very still.

In Sydney the London rooms of my memory house lose all their furniture, the videos go out the window, the blinds flip open, everything shrinks to bare floorboards which are easy to skip over, to add up to a breath before answering *Oh, jokes in the kitchen, and shopping, and a night at Madame Jojo's, a dash across town on the morning of the wedding to buy shoes.* Easy to walk other rooms. To be pulled on coconut leaves through the wet grass, the sleek rustle of it, the whooping. The laughing tilt of my mother's head, mock-scolded by market people. *Auntie, how can you say you're unlucky! Aiya, it's better to have girls, a son will be a slave to his wife, but girls love their mother forever.* To be taken to the house my mother grew up in and follow the adults on their slow ramble around the garden, sticking nails into pots of hydrangea to make their droopy heads blue. Stirring damp piles of grass and cuttings to flame. The abundant bougainvillea. That house with its servants' quarters was all polish and featherdusters, it was whispered voices and a kitchen filled to jostling with the sounds of water and vegetables and pots bubbling on the stove. The table was laid with more forks, knives and spoons than we knew how to use. Thick cloth napkins. *This is not your house, we are not your people, don't think you can run around as you like. Sit there and be still.* The press of the wall as my sister and I were made to squat in a corner. Statues of saints peering from glass cabinets high up on the walls. Parquet floors under bare feet.

In fact the servants' quarters were empty and the kitchen filled only with Mamanan dipping sliced bananas into batter, lowering them into the smoky frypan with her fingers almost skimming the oil. My sister and I watched with our mouths watering, knowing better than to tug at her sleeve. The days of white-clad servants, a cook, a cleaning girl, a nanny and a driver, were long gone by the time my father piled us into the car for our weekly visit, then set it purring with a honk or two outside the front gate. My mother dragged her feet down the driveway, she pushed the bolts home with a resounding thud. To my father's *They're family* she merely shrugged. In fact the floors of the old house were marble, those parquet squares so good for squeaking on belonged to another, to the one my sister and I learnt to tiptoe in early every schoolday morning. My mother swished ahead of us in her nightgown, smelling of herself and lavender, a finger pressed to her lips. One careless footstep and our rubber-soled shoes thumped and squeaked. *Quiet girls, your father's sleeping!* Our uniforms were ironed to sharp creases, two cups of hot milk sat on a kitchen ledge waiting to be gulped down. My sister drank first and I after, we wiped that cling-to-the-teeth powdered milk from our lips onto the backs of our hands. Then there were neatly cut sandwiches to be eaten and sometimes a half-boiled egg, and we were bustled to the loaf-shaped bus beep-beeping at the gate. Those were cool mornings, 5.45 a.m. with the house grey but already lightening and crows cawing south like a shadow of bombers. In the bus the smells of petrol and squashed bodies wrinkled our noses, the roof was so low our heads skimmed it all the way to the back with my sister leading and me concentrating, frowning, concentrating, and she anxiously turning to watch. *Don't do it, don't do it. Think of birds and butterflies and blue skies.* She thrust a crumpled plastic bag into my hand, but this was later, after days of heaving, my chest tightening, something squeezing through it and up my throat to be swallowed down, and swallowed, and never quite swallowed. Squashed as they were the other children slid away. *Don't do it, don't.* My sister carried my bag when I made it all the way to school, she slowed to keep pace with my weave-walking, then stopped as I leant against a lamppost, bending double, my breakfast a bitter rush splattering knees and shoes on its way. She stood rubbing my back, shifting from one foot to the other, while the girls streamed past. *Alright now? Have you finished? Hurry up, we'll be late.* In fact there were days I waved her ahead to watch the crowd swallow her in backslaps and arms around shoulders, friends offering to carry her things. I stood watching the swing of her ponytail, my bag where she left it, leaning against my leg.

In fact the girls making magic at the water fountain, balancing those styrofoam beads on that crest of water, were another pair of sisters, not us. In school my sister and I went our separate ways. We came home to schoolwork and television, frenetic talk at the dinner table, a whispered one late into the night: God and Truth and Family, teachers, hairstyles, what we wanted to do. The other pair of sisters were girls from my class, seated two rows ahead of me, their dark heads always bent to each other. They were identical twins. Instead of algebra and sheep farming I watched their secretive angle of heads, the way their arms linked, their habit of speaking for each other and walking precisely abreast. They went everywhere together, their skirts came to exactly two fingers above the knee. I sat behind the twins for a year. Later one wore gold hooped earrings and the other frizzled her hair, but for that one year I sat behind them, staring, filled with longing, they were exactly alike. In fact our childhood houses were also filled with solitary games. With hours of not speaking, of favourite toys hidden in malice, words scorching their way from our lips; either my sister or I stamping away from my mother with *You always take her side!* And speaking of facts, there are two other sisters I haven't even mentioned yet, though they too were a part of those childhood houses, twice did my sister and I sit quietly at the table because *Our*

Mummy's in hospital and we were big girls. Without complaint we ate the soy sauce omelettes and Chinese vegetables that were my father's specialities, cooked only when my mother was sick or away. We showed Mamanan the way to the market, walking one on each side of her, tricking her into buying sweets. There are two other sisters younger than me and though we were paired in twos of older and younger, two sets of *my sister and I*, for a number of years I was their ringleader, presiding over guinea pig burials in the garden and wild rides through a bandit-infested jungle on the kitchen table turned four-horse coach. The broomstick horses poking their shoe-faces in through the dining room window were made with them when my older sister suddenly became too big for such things. In fact it sometimes suits the shape of my memory if those two other sisters will do me the favour of sitting quiet, breathing even and unsneezing amongst the dusty cartons under the stairs. *In fact.* In fact if there's trouble with the architecture of memory where my sisters are concerned it isn't to do with winding corridors and too many closets, but false walls galore.

My mother's sisters, one married to the Secretary of the Turf Club, the other destined to become not a nun but a no-favourites auntie, lived in a house in *the European part of Kuala Lumpur*, then a city filled with streets named Templar, Freeman, Mountbatten and Yap Kwan Seng. The neighbours were expatriates, young couples on secondment from England, plantation managers, government advisers, other Eurasian families made good. An Indian man tended the garden, the driver was Malay, the cook was always Chinese. Of this time my mother speaks of dogs called Monday, Tuesday and Pharaoh, of racehorses and their sizes, gramophone records, lunch parties, the house filled with visitors arriving like her nieces and nephews, one after another, and servants who called her *Young Miss*. Later, the Rhode Island Red who was king of the back garden when times became tough and Mamanan insisted on raising her own fowl. The dog who sat pining on the front porch for months after her sister's husband died. My mother speaks of seaside holidays no longer possible, other sudden economies, the servants squeezing her hands before leaving with their faces reddened, their handkerchiefs well wrung. The house no longer filled with guests but with relatives armed with murmured advice and hand-patting, inevitable looks down the nose. Her youngest nephew hunched on the staircase long after bedtime, *But where? Where's Daddy, when is he coming back?* My mother wrapped her arms around him, she learned to walk quietly because even the sound of unquiet footsteps set her widowed sister trembling, voices above a whisper burst her poor aching head. My mother sat on the edge of the teak sofa, listening to the sisters explain why she couldn't stay at school. *We have to think of the children, Mary, there's school and then university overseas, it will be squeezing and scraping as it is. From now on you'll have to earn your keep.* Mamanan scolded and argued, but after a moment my mother merely nodded. She and Mamanan took over the kitchen while the sisters went out to teach, and one Christmas the Mrs Beaton's cookbook appeared by her bed. My mother learnt to drive, to ferry the children to school and back, to piano lessons and tuition, the pictures and shopping trips; she dressed cuts and listened to heartaches, she cleaned and polished, helped with plumbers, electricians and washerwomen, the countless details to do with running a house.

Years later, when my father was promoted from a travelling salesman to a sales executive and my mother's sisters were migrating to another country, he offered to buy the house in that European part of Kuala Lumpur which was then beginning to harbour well-to-do Chinese. The old house with its deep garden and circular driveway was long familiar with his creaky bicycle, then a succession of travel-worn cars. In schoolboy days my father plucked seeds from the angsana tree on his wobbly pedal down the drive. My mother's oldest nephew hailed him at the door and they settled to schoolwork together, laughed heartily at my father's attempts at grammar, scratched their heads over history and maths. Although they were classmates my father was the older, his schooling interrupted by the war. During breaks he wandered to the kitchen for milk and biscuits, he hung around my mother as she prepared the evening meal. He lay the bright red seeds on the kitchen table as though they were jewels. Sometimes he was allowed to stay. Before dinner he fixed stuck windows and doors off their hinges, he ran errands and sanded and painted when there was sanding and painting to be done. My father ran his hands over the polished furniture, he counted the rooms, marvelled at two to a bedroom which would fit many more. Years later, the sisters stared at him in disbelief. *But, Ray, we haven't made a final decision yet* they said, and *No, no, you couldn't possibly afford it*, and sold the house without telling him how much. The leftover furniture my mother inherited, along with Mamanan for a number of years while her immigration papers were being sorted out. The money sent every month for *looking after Mother for us* set her mouth in a sour line. That house is a bone my mother picks at in her soft afternoon voice, though it is morning or evening or sometimes long past midnight, with her sitting cross-legged on the carpet or echoing through the phone. *Why did he want it? They didn't want his money, why did he have to ask and ask?* My father's *They're family* merely makes her toss her head. My mother was famous for that disdainful toss of the head. For wicked pride that meant she was never grateful, and a habit of clamping her mouth tight. Of turning her face away when a concession was finally made, tickets bought for her also, or a length of cloth, or permission given for an outing for which at first she had begged. *No thank you, I don't want it, I'm not going. What makes you think I still want to go?* She stalked the house wrapped in a cloud both black and wordless, that shivered knives and forks in their drawers and skittered the kettle across the stove. The children kept out of her way with *Auntie Mary's in one of her moods* while Mamanan sighed and stood with hands on her hips. On our visits home my sister and I can only smile at that familiar toss of the head. We can only drape our arms around my mother, laughing, cajoling, using our fingertips to push the corners of her mouth back up. When my sister and I are visiting, my father makes a detour across the city so we can see what the old house is now like. Only its roof is visible over the bamboo hedge. My father looks at it wistfully, he backs the car for a better view. My mother looks, and looks away.

This is the situation, then, the youngest sister sitting on the hard edge of the teak sofa, her knees together, hands lying one beside the other, one on each knee. Her sisters sit opposite while her mother paces the length of the garden doors. Mamanan stops her angry undertone only to slap mosquitoes from her arms and neck. The sisters sit stiff and unbending, one with fingers pressed to her forehead, the other a sharp *Stop fidgeting!* every now and then. The future they paint is terrifying: my mother will be swallowed into a culture and language and people she doesn't know. Is this what they have raised her for? What will become of her? She will be a slave to a mother-in-law worse than any fairytale stepmother, she'll be worse than a slave. Someday the Chinaman will marry a younger wife. He is younger than she is, after all, and perhaps he will beat her, those people are known for that, and gambling, drinking, strings of children from God knows where, as well as opium pipes. He will find a young mistress, someone who speaks his language and knows his customs, who will turn his head completely and drive her out of his house. Her children will end up on the street. Has she thought carefully, has she considered all this? And how does she expect the family to get on without her, the younger children still at school, why can't she wait a little longer, hasn't she a shred of gratitude, after all they have done? My mother, the youngest sister, tilts her head forwards so her new fringe falls over her face. She has just cut her hair. That morning a woman in church came to a sudden stop before her, mouth fallen open, blocking her way. *My dear, why did you do it? Oh, why?* with a look to make my mother regret for an instant the thick reddish snake no longer curling to the small of her back. Her head feels so light, if she isn't careful, it will float past her sisters and Mamanan into the garden, away, but then my father's nicknames are in her ears. *Skeleton, Chinaman, Stick.* She imagines she is a statue, her body rigid, the words spilling over her head and shoulders like water over stone, but even after years of practice it is only her mouth she can keep perfectly still. *Stop fidgeting, I tell you!* one sister says, and the other sits with her face averted, and it seems a torrent of water before *Well, haven't you anything to say for yourself?* Even after years of practice my mother has to swallow before she can speak. Three pairs of eyes pin her to the edge of the teak sofa, that punishment seat she has sat in more times than she can remember, facing the three mothers she gained in Kuala Lumpur in place of the one who gave her away in Bangkok and the one who refused to leave her behind. In Kuala Lumpur Mamanan is a pale version of her Bangkok self, no longer does her arm shoot out in temper, no longer do her daughters shrink when she raises her arm. *Leave her to us, Mother, you spoiled her in Bangkok. You let her run wild.* The punishments the sisters resort to are the ones learnt from the nuns: interrogation, kneeling for hours, no talking allowed, a constant reminder of sins. In Kuala Lumpur Mamanan's eyes are filled to brimming so that the words that have been roaring on the end of my mother's tongue leave her in a whisper the sisters have to lean forward to catch. *If, as you say, all I'm good for is cooking and cleaning and looking after children, I'd rather do it in my own house.* The words are out and lie like broken glass between them, and for a moment all anyone can do is stare. Then Mamanan's shoulders are sagging as she comes towards my mother and one of the sisters is leaving with a sharp snap of the door, the other shrugging, sitting with her lips pressed together as though she will never again speak.

When my sister left for London she left behind her twin beds and a balcony door swirling with faces she'd painted in psychedelic colours that stopped people in the street, pointing, until my father whitewashed them away. She left a drawerful of trinkets I couldn't wait to get my hands on, bottles of perfume and moisturiser, tropical dresses held out with *Here, you like this, don't you? This one should fit*. She left me with one bed solely for sleeping on, the other for a growing spread of books, magazines and cushions piled high for a lounging read. An orchid from the garden in an ink bottle, soaking in brandy we swore we would one day drink, to remind us of our past. On the window sill was the only sign she hadn't ripped away, *To thine own self be true*. Her favourite popstar posters lay in untidy rolls in her side of the wardrobe, amongst clothes unable to be crammed into her suitcase, old schoolbooks, collections of stamps, badges and press cuttings painstakingly gathered over the years. A stuffed white rabbit almost as tall as she. *I'll take these next time*, she said, sighing, shutting the door. My sister had just turned eighteen. She held her plane ticket on the flat of her hand, stared at it from all angles as though it might suddenly disappear. The months before she left were passed in a whirl of motorbikes parked in the garden, visas and medical examinations, bank drafts, farewell dinners and parties, excursions to shops that specialised in winter clothes. My sister and I tried on the heavy coats together, we sneezed at woollen jumpers, sweated into the armpits and waistlines of close-knit shirts and trousers while my mother sat and watched. Laden with parcels we stopped for cendol and sago pudding at a coffeeshop and invariably some man or woman came over to chat and later slap their foreheads in disbelief. *For real, she's your mother? Wah, so youthful, you look like sisters, laughing and talking, having so much fun!* As she did on such occasions my mother merely smiled. My sister ticked items off a long list: London contact numbers noted, last farewells to be made, thank yous for the going-away presents opened then stuck into the wardrobe with all her other *next time* things. She printed the number and address of the college she was going to in texta over the phone.

Before she left we walked up to the shops for a last look round. The boyfriends roared their bikes after us, not finding us at home. They came to a stop with flourish, stood astride their bikes with sunglasses glinting, holding out spare helmets like lures my mother's sisters would assure her only bad girls took. My sister strapped on her helmet, grinning, and I stepped onto the other bike. *Goodbye shops*, she waved. *Goodbye bus stop. Goodbye kung fu movies, goodbye street!* Through the open doors of the local cinema we saw the once ruby-red curtains now faded and sagging. The aisles we once pelted down now seemed impossibly narrow, hard to imagine our joyous yelps finding groundnut shells on which to slide. Boys from the squatter village, now grown men, lounged on the cinema steps. They lifted their bony faces, pushed baseball caps from their foreheads the better to stare. My sister whooped from behind her sunglasses, she looped one arm around her boyfriend, raised the other in salute. At home my mother came to sit among the packed suitcases and travel bags. *Be good, take care of yourself*, she said, making a neat pile of the bits and pieces rejected at the last minute, crumpling the plastic bags and wrappers my sister had thrown any old where. *Don't forget your old mother and father, eh? Ring us when you get there, write as soon as you can.* At the airport she stood with my father, pressed against the railing, waving, two rounded specks very close together, which I would see from my own plane window in four years time, when my sister graduated and it was my turn to go. At home my mother swept the house from top to bottom, even though it was late. She ironed my sister's washing with the rest, cooked too much food for the evening meal. *Where do you think she is?* she asked every so often. *Over which sea?* Everyone went to bed early. *Aiya, we're getting old!* my father joked, following her up the stairs. *Soon it will be just you and me.* In my room I took down all my sister's posters, shoved them into the wardrobe with the favourite popstars now squashed under a mountain of left-behinds. In spite of my mother's protests my own things spread into and took over her half of the room.

My secret life, that eggshell shape, was the one my mother taught me. It was the space we held inside us, which belonged to us and us only, a pact between her and me. In it we kept resilient notes: all the words we heard, and kept hearing, either muffled or deafening, and the looks over shoulders, the lips pressed resolutely, the slamming of pots and pans and doors. *Wash your face at once, Mary, you look cheap. Where do you think you're going?* In it we kept a bundle of *What have we done to deserve this?* and *Why do you hate us?* as well as *Can't* and *Shame* and *Sinful*, and a swathe of *What will the neighbours think?* The sudden sharp image of a boisterous girl, not little, but not quite big, edging close enough to be included, *Me too! Me too!*, and only grudgingly allowed to join in. We kept my mother's particular terror *What mischief are you up to, Mary?* coming upon her dreaming on the doorstep or reaching for forbidden treats. *You'd better be good, or we'll give you to the gardener, we'll ask the gardener to take you, or the washerwoman. Your real mother did, don't think we won't.* A ride around the neighbourhood one night with a boy in a borrowed truck, an impulsive *Yes*, laughing and talking, turning into a session on the teak sofa with *How can you be so shameless?* and a week's retreat at the convent watched by sharp-eyed nuns as she knelt in the chapel with hands clasped in contemplation of *How*. My mother and I guarded those words and images as fierce as any treasure, we kept them in crystallised fragments she sometimes buried so deep I had to dig them out of her, to add to my own hoard. To stare at for hours slumped on the doorstep of a long-shut shophouse while she kept all the lights on at home. What extraordinary egg holds its shape past years of childhood slightings *No, not you, Mary, it's family business tonight*, through furtive sessions sitting in the garden with plans and promises spinning in her ears, *When we have our own children, Mary, boys or girls, we'll let them study, we'll give them everything we never had*, to emerge years later, whole and undented, unexpected amidst the security of wanted children and home-made curtains, in afternoons beginning with some careless word or action from my father, my sister or me ending in sudden silence, a turning, an angry toss of the head. A whispered litany over dusting, scrubbing and sweeping, digging its way with black earth and fertiliser into the tiers of potted roses my mother loved. *I am no one, I have nobody, I wish I was dead.* At first my sister and I followed her. We slunk around the house, tidying toys usually flung about and forgotten, watching her quick walk away from us. Giving up on afternoon stories, we tiptoed off to books and board games in our room. Even at an early age my sister and I understood the dangers involved in stumbling over a word or gesture that might turn out wrong. Like *Abracadabra!* any one word had the power to change my mother's whole face. Hours later we crept from our room to see if some other magic had managed to change it back. We set the table in silence, ate dinner with lip-smacking compliments to almost make her smile. Sometimes she lay in bed for hours, the curtains drawn, fearful headaches shivering her hands when she tried to raise them, her body breaking into sweat. My father came upstairs, sometimes with a doctor, sometimes tea and dry biscuits, tilting his head to send us out. *Girls, don't disturb your mother. She's just in one of her moods.*

The months after my sister left for London were passed in eddies of school and assignments, driving lessons, a holiday by the sea; kung fu movies as in the days of our childhood houses, my father insistent, my mother grumbling, and church every Sunday where they knelt on the polished pews. Having given up on communion and confession, I went to join the boyfriends with their bikes parked under the areca nut trees. The years passed in letters, photos and phone calls from my sister with the months stretching in between. Her packets of photos were opened like delicate gifts. My sister stared out from street parties, dressed in black, among people with ruddy cheeks and great mugs of beer. She sat on steps surrounded by pigeons, eating something out of a paper bag. Smiled in front of Tower Bridge, or on the steps of her college, her production crew around her, filming other students going past. Every day my mother flicked her way through the post. On letterless days she humphed back inside. *What's happened to that girl? You think she's got enough money, you think she's alright?* From three afternoon sisters sitting cross-legged with heads bent over Lego or a game of whispers, to three walking arm-in-arm down the sidewalk, stopping for a drink of young coconut water, we shrank to two whose specialty became an elaborate dance edging around each other. My mother and I stared anger and exasperation at the other, she dug into her secret space of *Can't* and *Shame* and *Sinful* for words she thought she'd never use. I took them from her as though they contained something precious, added them to my hoard, along with *Your sister knows better, your sister wouldn't, your sister, your sister, your sister –*

In my study in Sydney the geology of memory can be managed without its attendant dangers, those crystallised fragments belonging to my mother and me can be excavated with blurring but no permanent damage to the eye. Their layers laid out one over another as see-through as sugary curtains, as lace. In Kuala Lumpur those years after my sister left for London were passed in a kind of limbo of activity and inactivity: of school-leaving and part-time jobs, language and aptitude tests, countless trips to foreign embassies, nights either brazened or sneaked away with explosive homecomings – all these coupled with a *waiting* as necessary as some days it was endless, it was spent leaning against the railing of the upstairs balcony or dusting the curlicued bars on the windows, polishing the grandfather clock and inherited teak sofa until they shone. Sitting over a journal or writing pad, chewing on the end of a pen. In Kuala Lumpur my life was novels read completely at random, it was stories written, then slipped under a mattress, it was a mouth filled with eggshells so I could hardly speak. One wrong word and shards were spilling across the kitchen, pinning my mother to the counter with her shoulders sagged and tears trickling into the cut onions and carrots and beans. In Kuala Lumpur my secret life was a fury I did not know the words for, and so used any old words. Even in Sydney they sometimes come out too sharp. In Sydney I can name the fury, but never take it back. I can put *We want every chance for you* and *Nowadays girls are the same as boys* alongside entrance exams passed with distinctions and perfect scores, and still end up with those years of being reduced to nothing, neither ability nor talent nor conversation, nothing but my sex and the likelihood of the neighbours talking: the sum of what it was to be a girl.

In Kuala Lumpur I read my sister's letters to my mother the moment they arrived. I read the cards with funny captions, the *Happy Birthdays* and *Mothers' Days* and *Miss yous* that sometimes arrived too late. My sister was sorry she was too busy to write. Her course reports were excellent, the work was hard but rewarding, she was full of sights she'd never seen before, foods she'd never eaten, people who dressed and behaved so strangely we wouldn't believe in them unless we were there. These letters were a chatty travelogue, telling us nothing but the shiny surface of her life. On letterless days my mother came to sit on my sister's bed and stare over my shoulder at the journal I quickly snapped shut. She smiled, reaching to touch my forehead, filling my nostrils with mosquito-coiled evenings, a long ago and lavender dark. *When it's your turn, don't forget your old mother, eh?* In those days she was sometimes so overcome by headaches she lost her balance, she twisted her hip and had to have water drained from both knees. She swallowed a little blue pill every day. *Aiya, you girls are both the same, from the time you were little, always wanting to run away from Mummy. Always wanting to go. You're my daughters, my own, how do you expect me not to worry?* Sometimes the house shuddered with our slamming of doors.

When I talk of my sister it is her postcards I talk of, and her appearance, her clothes and accessories, her enormous brooches, the tiny black dresses and bright designer jackets she wears with bovver boots. I talk of her work that takes her to different countries so that the postcards appearing in my mailbox come stamped from Paris, Barcelona, Singapore, New York. My sister sits in meetings surrounded by men who raise their eyebrows, but jump when she speaks. There is a long scar by her nose and lips that I put there, neither hesitant nor thin. My sister is never still. Even as a child she was filled with a restless energy that swung her around flagpoles and into water fountains with parents and grandparents scrambling in her wake. My sister sings in bursts, like gunfire, she swings her arms as if rowing through air. She doesn't like fresh fruit except for pears shaped like pregnant women, and crunchy. She eats them when she's driving, tearing the skin with her teeth. Her hair is cut short with twirls over the ears like an opera singer's and her eyebrows are black and straight, no need for eyebrow pencils. She wears pink lipsticks that make her lips look stung. When she was sixteen a fortune teller told her she would find success in a faraway country, and marry twice. When she left us she changed the way she walked and dressed and talked, and also her name. For years I stubbornly used her old name. At Christmas she came home and sat in the garden smoking a pipe. She tamped the tobacco hard, teased tendrils from its surface for easy burning. She rang the day after her first wedding to tell us it was done. Once she fell off a motorbike and wore a beard of tiny black stitches for a week. Once I could never have imagined going anywhere without her, but nowadays we see each other only every two or three years, for two or three weeks. We live in cities at opposite ends of the earth, where we can pretend we are completely unique. When we see each other we hug briefly, we are shocked at the scrawled postcards and disembodied telephone voices turning into sisters we can touch. In London I sit in her kitchen eating cornflakes and chocolate biscuits with *Your sister, your sister, your sister* ringing in my ears. My mouth filled not with chocolate but the taste of eggshells so I look at her sideways, and critically. Only when I'm off my guard do I love her fiercely.

In London the lead up to the wedding is a hectic week of last-minute shopping, flowers, finalised menus, presents sneak-peeked at, the family arriving one after another, even my two younger sisters from out of those cartons under the stairs. The wedding is held at a small local church where the pastor scolds my sister at rehearsal for saying *Maybe* instead of *Yes*. There are blue shadows under her eyes on the morning of the wedding, which I inexpertly try to camouflage. I check her dress for loose powder, her skirt for threads, hover around her with hairbrush, lipstick and perfume. In her red halter and white skirt, she looks like a movie star from one of those kung fu epics we grew up on, a train of purple chiffon sweeping in her wake. In church the rows of men and women turn as the music starts and my father and sister enter with her looking to Marcus at the altar and he beaming in his morning suit. The church is filled with lit candles that catch the silver in my mother's hair. Later my sister and her husband manage to duck the confetti but not the cameras lurking at the door. In the photos we examine a week later everyone is smiling but caught in the crossfire, looking another way. In Sydney, two months later, I am woken in the middle of the night. *It's over*, my sister says. *We've separated, I wanted to tell you first. I wanted to tell you that time we went shopping, I wanted to say something. I never should've agreed to it in the first place.* I sit up in bed with the doona around my feet and my sister and I talk for an hour, we say *When* and *How* and *Why*, the things not even mentioned while eating those cornflakes and chocolate biscuits in her kitchen, and as usual we end with *Take care* and *Will you visit?* and *I'll try*. When I put down the phone I'm thinking of my shoes like boats in her London corridor, listening to that ringing in my ears *Your sister, Your sister* so clamorous all I could see was the movement of her mouth, no chance of hearing what she said, let alone what she did not say.

In Sydney we take my mother to visit her widowed sister who has settled twenty kilometres from me. My mother hasn't seen her for years, she hesitates on the doorstep before ringing the bell and is so surprised by her appearance that it takes her a moment to speak. They sit side by side on the sofa with *How are you?* and *Have another biscuit* and they fill each other in on who in the family is married, who is earning how much money, who has children, who has died. My mother's sister stares at us when she hears what my sister and I do for a living, she looks at my mother's fingers swollen from years of washing vegetables, scrubbing pots and pans and clothes. *Do you thank God, Mary? You've been so lucky, you married a good man. You should thank God every day of your life*. When we leave my aunt waves from the sofa and my mother is silent all the way to the car. All she says later is *Why, she has grown so small, she has shrivelled, I used to think she was big*, and then my mother laughs. My sister and I look at each other. We have been through the rituals of *How good to be here, How good to have you here*, and need only look, and raise an eyebrow, to smile. At home we go up to the roof to collect the washing. The flat roof of the apartment block is covered with a carpet of fake grass that crunches under our feet. The day is so bright and windy we have to shade our faces as we watch the city glinting in the sun. My sister can't believe this sun, she pulls up her sleeves, tucks them into the shoulders of her shirt. For efficiency we start at opposite ends of the clothes line, she ahead and me behind her, we begin to unpeg the sheets. The smell of clean washing is so inviting I have to slip between them, to stand breathing instead of unpegging, and so be caught by a sudden wild gust of wind. The wind flaps through the sheets like something alive and all too insistent, it pushes me a step forwards with my hands raised to the shape of my sister, caught by the same wind. For a moment all is white and sunlight between the two flapping sheets, the wind behind me, the sheet in front billowing as thin as membrane and almost as see-through, and only my sister's shape like an anchor, her arms spread out, holding me back. The warm smell of hours in the sun. Another gust and that front sheet, unpegged, lifts from the line, and my sister and I just manage to snatch it back. The cloth bucks and shudders in our hands, a sound like flying, but we hold it firm. We fold the sheets into halves and quarters, balance the washbasket between us and make our way downstairs.

A SCRAPBOOK, AN ALBUM

HELEN GARNER

'Children with the same family, the same blood, with the same first associations and habits, have some means of enjoyment in their power, which no subsequent connections can supply.'

JANE AUSTEN, Mansfield Park

I went to visit my four sisters, carrying a tape recorder and my imagined map of the family. It was unsettling to learn that each sister has her own quite individual map of that territory: the mountains and rivers are in different places, the borders are differently constituted and guarded, the history and politics and justice system of the country are different, according to who's talking. Now I'm in possession of the tapes and I don't know what to do with them. I thought of adding them to some as yet non-existent family archive – our father has burnt the slide collection – but they are too . . . blunt. I don't mean bitchy, though at certain points on each tape there are moments of intense silence followed by sharp laughter. I encouraged bluntness. But I was surprised. The ones I expected to hold back did not, while the usually talkative ones were discreet.

And because I, the eldest, was the one with the tape machine and the pen, this account lacks a blunt view of *me*. I got off lightly, this time. I tried hard to be irresponsible, to vanish, to be swallowed up by the texture of the writing. Because the one who records will never be forgiven. Endured, yes; tolerated, put up with, borne, and still loved; but not forgiven.

Already, a few weeks after we taped the interviews, regretful postcards, letters and phone calls are flying. 'What with my big mouth,' writes one, 'and your big ears . . .'

In the bunfight of a big family, each member develops a role. Everyone gets behind a persona and tries to stay there. Selective amnesia is required in order to maintain that persona. So the conversations on which this essay are based have stirred things up. And now I can't find a shape for the material I've got. The best I can do is a sort of scrapbook, or album. I certainly can't *analyse* my sisters. They keep taking over, bursting out of the feeble categories I devise to order the material: they keep heightening themselves, performing themselves with gusto. All I've done, really, is to tone them down. I feel panicky. We are five sisters and it doesn't even seem right to name us. The others wouldn't like it. 'The others', four women for whom I have feelings so dark and strong that the word *love* is hopelessly inadequate. I've used a chronological numbering system. We have one brother, by the way. He comes between sisters Four and Five. He's a chef. He makes the best lemon tarts in Australia. He has two sons. We love him, and we're proud of him. But he belongs to the male strand of the family: to a different species.

WORK

I note that I have immediately defined our brother by mentioning his job. It would never occur to me to do this about my sisters. Work is what interests us least about each other. Work is our separateness, what we do when we're apart.

We know that good manners dictate an interest in other people's jobs, so we ask each other perfunctory questions; but often the questioner has tuned out before the answer is complete. (Four is the exception to this. In childhood she seized the role of family clown, and every tale she tells is cleverly fashioned for maximum grip: 'He was wearing a rather bad pork-pie hat. Get the picture? A real "bohemian". So I say to him, "Can I *get* you something? Like the *bill*?" '

Otherwise, each sister's working life is a mystery to the others. Two of us were nurses, but I have never seen either of them in uniform. Four is in a band, which is more public, so she is often cranky because her sisters rarely come to hear her play. The three of us who write and publish live in a cloud of unknowing: has anyone in the family ever *read* our stuff? We are brilliant withholders. We behave as if we subscribed to Ernest Hemingway's dictum from Paris in the 1920s: 'Praise to the face is open disgrace.' Praise from each other and from our parents is what we really crave; but we will *not* gratify each other. Our pride in one another is secret and oblique. One winter Four's funk band collapsed and she had to take a job selling donuts from a van outside the Exhibition Buildings. Far from complaining, she kept me entranced with stories about her workmates and their customers. Once, on her night off, we were driving downtown to the movies and passed the van. She detoured in to say hullo, and came running back with a steaming bag of free donuts. Behind her back I brag about her: 'She can turn her hand to anything! She can pick fruit or pull cappuccinos. She's got no vanity about work. The people she works with love her because she makes them laugh.' But would I say these things to her face? That's not the way we do things, in this family.

'Three was complaining to me,' says Four, 'that whenever she visits Mum and Dad they never ask about *her* work, but are always reporting about the others, and praising them. Doesn't she realise that this is what happens to all of us? When *I* go out there, full of news, I have to sit in silence and be told in detail about One's latest book, or Five's new baby. I hate it, but I've got used to it.'

We are furious with our parents for their withholding, but *we* all do it too.

A SQUAD

Because I am the eldest, my sisters have always been behind me. My face has always been turned away from them, towards the world. I don't know what they looked like – that is, without photos I'd have no *memory* of what they looked like, though when I recently saw one of John Brack's etchings from the 1940s, of a tiny, sulking schoolgirl, I recognised her at once as me or one of my sisters: the chunky stance, the shoulders high with dudgeon, the scowling brow, the tartan skirt and the hair brushed back and held to one side with a ribbon. And yet I also have no memory of a time when they weren't all there – the first three, anyway. I have always been part of a squad. There are photos of me as a tiny baby, mad-eyed, box-headed, being held correctly positioned on the bent arm of my young, nervous mother, or bundled with my back against the chest of my grinning father, my blanket awry, my beady eyes popping with the force of his hug (see *The Favourite*, below); but now, when I look at these pictures, I am completely unable to believe that outside the frame my sisters aren't hanging around, squinting in the sun, picking at their knee-scabs or twiddling their ribboned 'bunches', waiting for me to climb down and turn back into a kid and come outside to play.

LAUGHTER

Whenever I try to live in another town, my phone bill rockets; and when I look carefully at the breakdown of the call times, I see that I make the largest number to my sisters between the hours of four and five p.m. – that is, after-school time. I am fifty but I still have this habit, this longing to hear their stories of the day. I want them to make me laugh.

Two women are sitting in a fashionable cafe when their sister walks past, carrying a briefcase and looking cool and purposeful. She does not look in, but passes wearing the kind of expression one adopts when passing the grooviest cafe in town without looking in. The two sisters inside don't speak, but lower their heads to the table in silent fits.

But we don't laugh *at* each other. We laugh *about* each other.

They knew that Virginia Woolf was about to crack up again when she wrote in her diary that she and her sister 'laughed so much that the spiders ran into the corners and strangled themselves in their webs'. Perhaps her case was extreme but I cannot say that such laughter is unknown to me and my sisters. There is something ecstatic, brakeless, about the way we laugh together. We laugh in spasms and paroxysms. Almost anything – a glance, a word, a mimicked grimace – can act as a trigger. When any (or all) of us are together we are quivering in readiness for the thing that will push us off the edge of rational discourse into freefall over a bottomless canyon of mirth; laughing together is a way of merging again into an inchoate feminine mass. (Again? When was this previously the case?)

Perhaps 'hysterical' *is* the right word: I've heard this wild laughter among nurses, waitresses, nuns. If you are not included in it, it can be alarming – not because you are the butt of it; it's not 'bitchy' laughter – but because there is something total about it, shameless; it's a relaxation into boundarylessness. Of course, as a spectacle, it is probably boring. It is ill-mannered of us to indulge in it in company. Sometimes two or three of us will withdraw from the table, at a big gathering, and be found in another room shortly afterwards, doubled up in weak, silent laughter. 'What, what is it?' the discovering sister will beg. 'What? Oh, tell me!'

THE FAVOURITE

'I was the favourite for eighteen months,' says One. 'I think I'm the only one who can categorically and objectively state that. A short blessed period which ended when Two was born and usurped my position. I've spent the rest of my life, in a warped way, trying to regain it through *merit*. Fat chance. This is the theory of the driven, perfectionist eldest child, and I believe in it.'

'I remember distinctly,' says Two, 'feeling that I was the favourite child. One and Three were in the poo for some reason, and I remember thinking, "Mum and Dad aren't cross with me – therefore they must like me best." It was a transitory feeling. Two years ago, when Mum and Dad were coming back from overseas, some of us went to the airport to meet them. Three had gone to the toilet, and they came out of the customs hall before she got back. We had the regulation pecks on the cheek, then Dad looked around and said "Where's Three?" He saw her coming from a long way away, and he put out his arms to her while she walked towards him. He gave her a huge hug.'

'Two turned to me as we all trooped towards the carpark,' says Three, 'and she said to me, "You always were his favourite." What Two doesn't know is that for five years I'd been chipping away at Dad, after watching Grandma die lonely in that nursing home, looking for affection from anybody who'd give it, because she'd wasted her chances in life – I was with her when she was dying, and I couldn't *bear* it. I thought, "I'm not going to wait till Dad gets that old. I'll teach him if it kills me." So for five years I'd been *insisting* on giving him a hug and a kiss every time we met or parted. I even knocked on the car window and made him wind it down, when he'd got into the car to avoid doing it. I'd been pushing through that barrier. I was on some kind of mission, thinking, "I *will find* something on the other side of this." I didn't even need to earn acceptance or approval any more. I just wanted to break through that lonely barrier around him. I *never* felt the favourite.'

'Oh, Two was the favourite,' says Four. 'It was obvious. She was always the golden-haired girl. She was given a twenty-first at the Southern Cross. The *Beatles* had just been staying there. In 1965 it was the grooviest place in town. Later I remember Five being Dad's favourite. Ohh – indubitably. When she was little.'

'Everyone loved me endlessly,' says Five. 'I was born so many years after Four that I didn't have to fight anybody for anything. But sometimes now I feel a rather pathetic figure in the family – like the dregs of the barrel. As if what I've got to offer is somehow less. Everything's been done before, and better. If I'm patronised or ignored, I bow out. With my friends I feel more entertaining and clever than I do with my sisters – more relaxed and free.'

'Once,' says One, 'I was in the kitchen at Two's with Five and our brother. And in whispers we agreed that we were probably the three favourites: the eldest, the youngest, and the only boy.'

'Still, I had the best rollerskates, I thought,' says Three. 'Mine were German, and yours were only English.'

Are we in competition? And if so, what for? What's the prize?

LIKENESS

Once, during a visit, Three and One were standing behind Three's children who were watching TV. One grabbed the scarf Three had on, and Three put on One's denim jacket. Three called out, 'Hey, you kids!' The kids gave a perfunctory glance, looked back at the television, then swung round in a slack-jawed double-take. Yes, just for a split second they couldn't tell the difference. Why did Three and One find this so satisfying?

What if each sister should keep an album of unflattering photos of the others? 'Ooh, she'll hate this. She looks like something by Francis Bacon.' No, we're not really that kind of family. But we all examine photos with meticulous care, glancing up with narrowed eyes at the subject, and down again.

We look like each other. Strangers stare at us in the street and say, 'You wouldn't be So-and-So's sister, by any chance?' For some, obviously, this is more flattering than for others. One, as eldest, embodies a version of the others' fates: a heavy burden. Covertly we check each other for signs of ageing, signs of *giving in*. When One started to wear what in our family are known as 'old duck sandals', a tremor of apprehension ran down the ranks. But our ex-sister-in-law saved the situation. She looked at the sandals for a long time, then said, 'Yes, they're daggy all right. But they're so daggy that they're almost *clever*.' A week later Four turned out to a party wearing an identical pair.

On tape our voices sound eerily similar.

Each sister manifests for the others a version of our common looks. Each performs her version of the inherited character. Each is a cautionary tale for the others, in different ways and at different times.

One day, when one of my sisters came and complained to me bitterly and at length, laying out in front of me what our mother used to dismiss as 'some great tale', I watched her in growing dismay. I saw the expressions that passed over her face and felt the sympathetic movements of my own facial muscles. I saw *myself*, my rigidity and pride, my pleasure in being aggrieved, my drive to power. And then, as we were saying goodbye on my verandah, under a climbing rose in bloom, each of us turned as if choreographed, picked a flower, and thrust it through the other's buttonhole. Perhaps after all we are not so horrible.

And it did happen that the 'rejected' one, when her life seemed to have collapsed, went to church one Sunday morning, wanting to be absolved, comforted, blessed, she didn't care any more who by. She went up to the communion rail and got down on her knees. She looked up, as the chalice approached her, and saw that the robed person offering her the wine was *her sister*.

'I saw you recognise me,' says One. 'It rocked you – I saw it go through you like a lightning bolt. I thought you were going to keel over.'

'I didn't even know you were in the church,' says Three. 'And when you put out your hands and turned up your face, for a second I thought it was myself.'

HOUSE

A certain humility is appropriate in a sister's kitchen. Respect is owed to the one wearing the apron. We enter each other's kitchens, however, as if we were coming home to our mother: straight to the biscuit tin, the nut jar, cram in a handful and stand there chewing, leaning on the cupboard and talking.

Our kitchen and household customs, while not identical, resemble each other strongly: the use and abuse of the dishcloth, the order in which things are done, the theory of storage.

But when Three has been minding Five's new baby, Five remarks, upon changing a nappy after the baby-sitter has gone home, 'Three always does the pins backwards.'

We are drawn to stand in each other's bedrooms. Perhaps it's simply for the scent of the place where a sister's body has slept. Even a husband's smell can't mask the deep familiarity of the first person you shared a room with. I love to put my head on my sisters' pillows, and breathe in. I like the smell of clean skin, something sweet and cottony. Maybe that smell is not just sisterly, but motherly.

'When I got my first period,' says Two, 'I told One. She laughed. But then she was nice, and took me out to the toilet and showed me how to put the pad on. I didn't tell Mum. Do you remember the toilet, at that house at Ocean Grove? It was like a brown coffin.'

'Do you mean the room, or the toilet itself?'

'The room,' says Two patiently. 'It was painted brown, and sort of curved.'

'I don't remember that,' says One. 'I thought it was white.'

Two visits One and they discuss the problem of curtains for the big back windows of One's kitchen. 'It faces south,' says One, 'so it doesn't get direct sun.'

'South *west*,' says Two, firmly. 'That's south *west*, so it *must* get direct sun, late on a summer afternoon.'

'Oh . . . yes, I suppose it does,' says One, 'in summer.'

Two is very happy about this. She sits down at the kitchen table and says, with a big smiling sigh, 'I'm *much* more of a sun and moon person than you, aren't I!'

Sisters have no truck with one another's finer feelings. Once I visited a friend and helped her in the kitchen where she was preparing a meal. I remarked, as I laid out the cutlery, 'This table is too low. Whenever I sit at it I knock my knees. You ought to get a higher one.'

She turned round from the bench and stared at me; her face was blank with shock.

'What's the matter?'

'That table,' she said, 'has been in my family for generations. I *love* that table.'

'Oh – sorry!'

We went on with our work. A week or so later she brought it up again.

'I think I was so shocked,' she said, 'because I've got no sisters. I'm not used to that bluntness. *Thwack* – you just *hit* me with it. But I realised later that you hadn't meant to offend me.'

There are no beloved historic objects in our family. There is no family home. Every time our mother gets settled somewhere, our father gets itchy feet and they sell up and move on. They have moved so often that some of their children have not even visited every house they've lived in.

GOING IN TO BAT

'I remember,' says Four, 'when some hoon friends of Five's flatmate terrorised her one time, when she was home alone. After they'd gone she rang me up. Her voice was so faint that I thought she'd been raped. So One and Five and I found out the name of the main hoon, and we put on our best black jackets and drove out to his parents' house where he lived, to sort him out. Remember – it was a horrible cream brick veneer house, with a shaven lawn and no trees, and we presented ourselves at the front door, after dinner one evening, and asked for him. And when his mother said he wasn't home, One said, in a polite and icy voice, 'Perhaps we could have a word with *you*, Mrs So-and-so.' She sat us down in her lounge room on some fancy chairs, and we dobbed her son, in detail. She was struggling to look as if she didn't believe us; but I bet he *was* home. I bet he was hiding in his bedroom, letting his mother take the rap.'

'I was so nervous,' says Five, 'that I kept letting off huge odourless farts into the upholstery.'

'It didn't do much good, I guess,' says Four, 'but we shrieked and yelled all the way home down the freeway. And probably went out dancing for the rest of the evening.'

'I went in to bat for you, Two,' says One, 'at Ocean Grove State School in the 1940s, when someone had swindled you out of your best swopcard. I marched over and forced her to swop it back.'

'I don't remember that,' says Two.

'Three took me on a secret trip to Sydney,' says Four, 'so I could meet my boyfriend when he'd gone interstate to university. We went on the train. We walked around Kings Cross.'

'One took me to Bright and Hitchcock in Geelong to help me buy my first bra,' says Three. 'She protected me from those thin ladies in black with the tape measures round their necks. Because I didn't really have much to put *in* a bra. I needed one for other reasons.'

'When I came back from Sydney to live,' says One, 'Two arrived at my front door with a huge picnic basket full of wonderful food.'

'I was responsible for Five,' says Two, 'when Mum and Dad put her into boarding school so they could go overseas. Mum said to me, "You were wonderful to Five." I was, too. I liked doing it – but sometimes I get this narky feeling that I'd like to send in an account.'

'Three dared to come to my first wedding,' says One, 'when Dad forbade everyone to go. And she took it right up to Dad when he called my husband a conman.'

'Wait till your father dies,' says somebody's husband.

'You'll be like the Baltic states at the collapse of the Soviet Union. You've been formed and bound together in opposition to him. When he goes there'll be hell to pay.'

'Let's try to keep it on sisters,' says One. 'Don't let's talk too much about our parents.'

'But aren't they sort of the point?' says Five.

'Yes, but it's obsessive. We all swerve and swerve back to our parents. I want us to talk about being sisters, not daughters.'

OTHER PEOPLE'S SISTERS

I mention to a friend that I am trying to write this. She remarks, 'The best way for sisters to get on is to talk about their parents.'

Some sisters are sisters with a tremendous, conscious, public conviction. I remember a woman I knew, years ago, who would get up from the lunch table and retire to her room for the afternoon, saying 'I'm going to write a letter to my sister.' We felt respectful, and tiptoed round so as not to disturb her. She would emerge, hours later, looking purged, satisfied, and slightly smug.

Another friend, one of whose sisters recently died in a freak accident, says to me, 'I've lost our shared childhood. I depended on her memory. I loved going out with her. When we walked down the street together with our youngest sister, the three of us, I used to be so proud and happy. I used to feel we were invincible – that nothing could touch us.'

This is the kind of story I think of as sisterly: Once a woman was driving along a street in West Melbourne when she was attacked by severe abdominal pains. She tried to ignore them and drove on, but they became so violent that she was obliged to park her car outside a friend's house and stagger in, doubled over, to lie on a bed. Gradually the pains abated. When she was able to go home, she phoned her mother for a chat and learnt that, the same day, her sister had given birth to her third child in Geelong, and had had to agree to a hysterectomy because of unstoppable bleeding.

A striking example of telepathic contact, yes; and it happened, in our family. But the story is rarely told, sixteen years later, because this gut empathy had no practical application. The flaw is that when Three needed help, after that hysterectomy, none of the rest of us thought of offering any; she did not feel able to ask for it, and thus got none. The spirit of our family is 'Pick up your lip before you trip over it.' Is that sisterly?

THE DIFFERENT ONE

I asked my sisters, separately, to characterise themselves. Each of them, in slightly varying phrases, saw herself as the different one.

'I felt for years the rejected one,' says One. 'I couldn't go near the place without getting into a fight with Dad. But when I sent Mum a birthday telegram signed *The Black Sheep*, she got upset.'

'I remember feeling I was very different from the rest of you,' says Two. 'I was the first to marry and I lived in the suburbs, whereas you all (except Three) saw each other a lot and lived that sloppy rock&roll life, which was anathema to me, with a husband and two kids. I'm the only one who doesn't vote Labor. At family gatherings I still feel out of it, a bit. I dress differently.'

'I was always the odd one out,' says Three. 'I was a nuisance to One and Two, when I was little. Later I was the only one interested in having a spiritual life. Two came into the bedroom once and found me on my knees. I don't know which of us was more embarrassed. Then I struck out on my own and went to Papua New Guinea straight from school, and worked on the mission. It was a great shock, after growing up in a middle-class family. I was always looking for a way of doing life more simply. But then I burrowed into a conventional marriage.'

'I got the short end of the stick,' says Four, 'because I was the fourth girl. They must've looked at me and thought, "Bloody hell – not another girl!" I've always thought that was the basis of my problem with Dad. Remember how when he was trying to tell childhood stories about everyone, at his birthday party? He couldn't remember anything about me to tell. I've constantly felt the odd one out – *constantly*. And I feel it now, specially since Five had a baby, because I'm the only one without children, and the only one who never wanted any.'

'I,' says Five, 'am the odd one out only in the sense that I'm the youngest by ten years. Otherwise I don't feel that way at all. Oh – if you all get together and I haven't attended, I feel miffed or excluded. But I must have received a lot of attention when I was young. Mum and Dad had more time to spend with me. They took me travelling round the world with them. My relationship with them is different from the others.'

WHAT DID YOU PAY FOR THOSE?

We are not so different that we can't wear each other's clothes. When one sister arrives at another's house, the first thing they do together is dash to the bedroom and start trying on shoes.

At Christmas, One and Two arrive at Five's house for the big family dinner. They walk down the hall and become instantly aware of a certain quality of silence issuing like smoke from one of the bedrooms. They rush in. There stand Four and Five, bent over a table, heads together, backs to the door, working hard at something. They glance up as One and Two barge in, but their eyes are blank with concentration and without speaking they return at once to their task. One and Two push in beside them and see what is on the table: Five's six-month-old daughter, flat on her back, looking patient but slightly puzzled. Four and Five are trying to squeeze the baby's fat feet into a tiny pair of red leather boots. The boots are much too small, but Four and Five will not accept this. Quivering with suppressed giggles, they lace and tug, applying force to the leather and the flesh as if the baby's life depended on it. It is a bizarre initiation rite into the family passion for shoes. Shoes bought in haste, that don't fit.

One day in winter, One leaves her muddy Doc Martens on the front verandah. Next morning they are gone. She searches everywhere, then curses thieves and gives them up for lost. Several days later, in the afternoon, the doorbell rings. One opens the door and sees Four on the mat, beaming at her with a wicked look. Instinctively One's eyes drop to Four's feet. On them are the missing Docs.

'That'll teach you,' says Four suavely, 'to take better care of your possessions.'

In David Jones' 'perthume' department, Two says to One, 'Here – let me squirt this on you, in case I hate it.'

Four possesses an absolutely reliable brutality when it comes to clothes. 'Should I buy these trousers, Four? Look, they're only $30.' Four runs a cold eye over them, and turns away. 'Buy them if you want to look like a *stump*. Like a *mallee* root.'

One and Three enter a shop. Three scans it, then heads unerringly for a rack of dark, sober, important-looking garments. One grabs her by the back of her jacket and steers her firmly towards a row of pretty, soft, pale, flowery dresses. The expression of suspicion, self-dislike and severity on Three's face, while she tries on a dress and examines herself in the mirror, reminds One so much of herself that it squeezes her heart. Three buys a dress. Next time One approaches Three's house, she sees a slender, long-haired girl standing out on the pavement, with the wind swaying her loose skirt. 'Oh, how pretty,' thinks One. She gets closer and sees that it's Three, aged 45, wearing the dress they chose together.

A Deeply Wounded Postcard

If there are five of you, you form a complex network of shifting alliances.

'For six months,' says Five, 'I'll mostly hang out with Four; then she'll say or do something that shits me, but instead of slugging it out with her on the spot, I'll show her the door in a restrained manner and then get straight on the phone to One: "Can you *believe* what Four just said to me? Fuckin' bitch!" And then I'll move over to a different camp, for a while.'

'I was outraged,' says Three to One, 'by what you said about that African movie as we came out into the foyer. I'd been so moved by it – and you ruined it, in one smart crack. I had to get away from you, before you completely destroyed it for me. I came home and wrote you a letter about it. Which I didn't send.'

'I wrote Three a terrible letter,' says One, 'and I posted it. I quaked for a week, then she sent me a deeply wounded postcard. I apologised, and it was never mentioned again. But ooh, I'd love to have a fight with her.'

'Sometimes,' says Five, 'I despise myself after I leave one sister's house, thinking about how I've curbed my behaviour in her company. To please her. It's so easy to slip into a style of dialogue that suits the one I'm visiting.'

'Yes,' says Four, 'and when you get home you write the letter.'

'Five had the nerve,' says One, 'to write me an extremely snippish letter. I had to go for a walk to calm down. And then I wrote her a scorcher which said all the things I'd been bottling up for years and hadn't had the nerve to say before. I said, You listen to me. I said, How dare you. I said, I should come over and kick your arse right round the block. That sort of thing. I censored the worst bits, and then I posted it.'

'When I got the letter from you,' says Five, 'I was paralysed. I also noticed you'd cut bits off the bottom of one page, so I realised there'd been even worse things. I sat on the end of my bed. I could hardly move for half an hour.'

'The bits I cut off,' says One, 'I pasted into my diary. That's how I remember what I originally said.'

'Why *don't* we yell at each other?' says Four.

'Because,' says One, 'we're so in love with the idea of our family continuing that to speak truly and honestly would jeopardise it.'

'Isn't that a bit pathetic, though? I think we should yell at each other.'

'You start.'

'All right. "Get out of my sight, you moll." How's that?'

'This is *serious*, Four – do you mind?'

'OK. Sorry. But you did yell at me once – don't you

remember? I came over to borrow some money and you lost your temper.'

'I remember now. I yelled at you that you were so selfish you never asked me how I was, or anything about *my* life – all you did was whinge about *your* problems. You bawled and howled, it was dreadful, and I said, "I'm sorry if this hurts you," and you said, howling away, "It's all right, because I need to know why nobody likes me." And that of course was so tragic that *I* started bawling, and then you looked at me with your red eyes and said in a weird, polite, choked sort of voice, "And how's work going lately?" We both cracked up laughing – and then I lent you $500 and you went home.'

'I had a fight one night with Two,' says One, 'outside Trinity Chapel after evensong. We'd gone to hear the choir. I'd left a cake in the oven before I came out of the house and I was worried about getting home in time. I was strapping on my bike helmet, and Two started in on me about the Old Testament readings, which had been about the parting of the Red Sea. She said, "It's awful. It's *racist*." I said, "Oh, don't be ridiculous." She said, "I am *not* being ridiculous! Imagine if *you* were an Egyptian and had to sit there listening to that!" I lost my temper and yelled at her. She didn't turn a hair. You can say *anything* to Two – she never takes umbrage, she just keeps on arguing. I realised how grotesque I must be looking, scowling and red-faced with my hideous helmet on, and I broke off and said "I've got to go straight home." Two said, "Yes, go on – go home to your *cake*." I pedalled away, to cross the university grounds, and I suddenly thought, "Goodness – we've had a fight!" But I didn't feel bad. I felt great. I felt exhilarated. And I yelled back to her, "The music was fabulous!" I could see her rippling along behind the fence railings as she strode back to her car – she didn't answer, but just waved and kept walking. I zoomed home on my bike, thinking, "Hey! Fighting's not so bad!" The next day I wrote her a postcard saying something to that effect. And she sent me one back, quite cheerful and dignified, saying "That wasn't a fight. It was a *disagreement*." '

'Yes, you can really have a fight with Two,' says Five. 'There's something thrilling about her bluntness. She's got no shame. And she doesn't get so *personal*.'

'It must be because she's done assertiveness training,' says One. 'I think it must teach you to do your best to get your own way, but if you don't, you don't sulk. You just cop it. It's quite impressive, in a gruesome sort of way.'

'I fought with Four,' says Five. 'It was very beneficial. I realised I wouldn't be able to go *on* with Four unless we had a fight. I said dreadful things. She was crying and crying – but she was taking it all on board. I had to respect her for that. I kept trying to put her to bed. She said, "Fuck you – I don't *want* to go to bed!" But I kept on trying to force her to.'

'That would've been because of what I said about Whatsis-name, I'm sure,' says Four. 'He was a *pret*-ty vile guy, which Five later came to realise . . . whereas I knew it all along, and said so.'

'Three and I were building up to a smash,' says One, 'but we sidestepped it. She played the martyr, basically, and I panicked and became feeble and began to appease her.'

'We're always very quick to apologise,' says Three.

'That's our way,' says One, 'of keeping everything on a safe, superficial level. We say, "I've hurt her. I'll call it rudeness and say I'm sorry." Whereas if we were really going to have some form of intimacy, we'd yell at each other – "damn it, get that look off your face!" '

'I hold back from fighting, usually,' says One, 'because if I say to my sister what I really think about her, I'm licensing her to tell me what she really thinks about *me*. And I don't know how to defend myself against that. I'm afraid of it. Because sisters don't subscribe to each other's mythology. To the myths of each other.'

'I'm scared of you,' says One.

'I'm scared of you, too,' says Three.

They laugh, and look away. Then they glance at each other again, curiously. Tenderly.

THEATRE

There is a tendency in our family to brood on slights. Each likes to tell a story in which she appears more sensitive and more hard done by than another. We would rather be wounded, and glory in our outraged sensitivity, than take it up to the offender and make a protest to her face. Thus we end up with a series of shrines. Each of us (with the exception perhaps of Two, who is more robust, frank and fearless) keeps a little shrine to herself, with a little lamp inside it eternally flickering, and the oil that feeds it is the offences dealt out by her sisters. The misplaced smirk, the thoughtless crack is stored away, and for a while the little ego-lamp burns more brightly – until there's the shift, when the incident is related to one of the other sisters as a story, constructed and pointed with the primary aim of provoking laughter and a momentary sense of alliance. It becomes another chapter in our fanatically detailed, multi-track story about ourselves, which is hilarious, entertaining, appalling, obsessive. It is related in a secret language composed of joke pronunciations, silly accents, coded phrases whose origins were forgotten long ago but which are heavy with meaning and will always raise a laugh.

We are major characters in the stories of each other's lives; we are all acting in an enormous comedy that will go on till we die. It has no audience but its own performers: our children and husbands roll their eyes and walk out of rooms. Its time scale is an endless, immediate, now.

OBSESSION AND INTIMACY

'Once I was raving on,' says One, 'about my family to a bloke I know who's got four brothers. After a while he started twisting in his seat, and then he burst out, "Anyone would think you were the only person in the world who had a family!" I felt foolish. But I sort of couldn't *help* it.'

'I have to hold myself back,' says Five, 'with anyone I meet, from talking about our family. My friends are probably driven bonkers by the way I *go on* about it. They never seem to need to talk about theirs. I prod them. I say, "I didn't know you had a brother. Tell me about him." But they say they can't be bothered. "Why?" "Because he's boring." How can a brother or a sister be *boring*?'

'I think it's something wrong with *us*,' says One. 'I've spent my life trying to have friendships outside the family which will provide as much intimacy as I get from my sisters. It's a doomed enterprise. So I keep crashing and smashing and falling out with my friends. They can't stand the demand for intimacy and attention. I bore them, I irritate them, I wear the friendship out.'

'I don't think intimacy is the problem,' says Two. 'It's because you're too bossy. We're all too bossy.'

'*I* never got this intimacy from our family,' says Three. 'A lot of people say they envy me having four sisters – but no one ever hugged or cuddled, to comfort. It wasn't done. I was at a friend's place recently when her older sister came round, looking wretched. Between our sisters, a rough joke would've been made – Come on, pick up your lip before you trip over it! But the younger one had a good look and said, "Ah – what's the *matter*?" The older one shed a few tears and: "Life's too difficult. I'm trying to work, and there's the baby, and I have to do a course if I want to keep my job – it's too much for me." And the younger one said, "Oh, come here" – and sat her sister on her *lap*. Can you imagine any of us doing that? Then they ran a bath and got in it together. I heard them laughing and shrieking. I felt terribly envious. Maybe you others had that sort of closeness. I never did. When I had a hysterectomy, I was abandoned. See? You hardly even remember it. One came down and minded the boys for a couple of days, but the rest of the time I was on my own, with a new baby and two toddlers, too weak to get out of bed. It was . . . desolate. I learnt not to look for help from the family.'

'Yes, that's shameful,' says One. 'But do you realise how perfect your marriage seemed, from the outside? You looked as if you had everything sewn up. You didn't ask for help. There's an art in asking.'

'I know how,' says Three, 'but I wouldn't.'

'Why?'

'I was afraid of indifference.'

'*Would* there be indifference, if you showed weakness?'

'It's not weakness,' says Three. 'It's need. It's better not to show need, if you're not going to get your needs met. I've learnt that. I worked out where people were going to care enough, and I went there.'

'It *is* rather uneven,' says One. 'I tried to tell Four my troubles once – we were driving downtown in a car. I talked for five minutes, and she cut across me and said, 'Oh, shut up – you sound exactly like Mum.' But whenever anything goes wrong in *her* life, the first thing she does is pick up the phone and dial my number.'

Four is the witty one. But as a child she was a tremendous howler. At the slightest setback she would throw back her head and roar; tears would squirt out of her eyes and bounce down her fat cheeks. One, Two and Three used to hold up sixpence at breakfast time, saying, 'You can have this tonight – but every time you cry, we're going to dock you a penny.' By teatime Four would be once more heavily in debt.

'If we cried when we were little,' says Two, 'Mum used to say "Stop it, you great *cake*." '

'I don't remember that,' says Five.

'Of course you don't,' says Two. 'You weren't born yet.'

'Three,' says Two, 'was the painful little sister we used to run away from. Once she tried to bribe us. She said, "I'll give you throopence if you let me come with you." But we took no notice and kept on running.'

'I remember that,' says Three. 'I can remember the feeling of the wire of the gate under the soles of my feet, as I hung over it and watched you two disappearing up the road. At least, I think I remember it. Maybe it's only because the story's been told so many times.'

'Maybe,' says One, 'it never happened at all.'

ENDEARMENTS

Because endearments were never used in our family (Plymouth Brethren two generations back on our mother's side; grim-jawed Mallee stoicism on our father's), it has taken us all our lives to learn to say *dear, darling, sweetheart*, without irony.

'At school,' says One, 'when I was a boarder, I was sick with envy of girls who got letters from their parents that started with the word *Dearest*.'

A few years ago, Four sent One a telegram: 'Dearest Darling, happy birthday, from your Darling.' The telegram was read, marked, learnt and inwardly digested, then thrown into the rubbish bin. That night a strong wind blew, and overturned the bin into the running gutter. Next morning an angry young man knocked on One's front door. He thrust the crushed and sodden telegram in her face: 'Is *this* how you treat a man's heartfelt declaration of love? Shame on you!' 'It's not a man!' cried One. 'It's my *sister*.' He stared at her strangely, and stamped out the gate.

If one of us uses an endearment on the phone to a child, a friend, a lover, while a sister is in the room, she glances nervously behind her to make sure she is not being mimicked. None of us would dream, however, of mocking someone for doing this. In fact, we would (I believe) like to pet and treasure each other, to pour out floods of sweet words. But we are all engaged in the same struggle against inherited embarrassment, against a terrible Australian dryness. We maul and stroke each other's children: it's the closest we can get. And our children submit to their aunts' possessive handling with patient smiles.

CLASS

From the middle of the middle class there are paths leading in both directions. A family can rise or fall in class over twenty years, so that its eldest child is brought up at one level, and its youngest in quite another.

'I used to escape from the bedlam,' says Two, 'by going to my friend's place over the back lane. Her father listened to opera, and her mother always did beautiful ikebana flower arrangements that I loved—she was so creative. They had posh accents. The parents didn't just have single beds, like our parents did – they had separate rooms. I liked their accoutrements: engraved silver, crystal, a back sitting room. They had two spaniels called Kismet and Ophelia. They were what I aspired to be: Geelong Grammar posh people. We were down market. I wished our parents said *dahnce* and *cahstle*. Three always disapproved of my lifestyle, later on. Once I said to her, "I'd like to have a marblised wood dining table. I suppose they must be really expensive" – and she came back at me: "Even *poor* people have dining tables, you know!" – almost as if she thought my whole life was devoted to . . . acquisition. It probably is! I wouldn't deny it! I don't care about that now, but I used to.'

'Once I went with Two to a department store,' says Three, 'to buy our kids some pyjamas. I headed straight for the bargain bin, and she made a beeline for the quality shelf. When we met at the cash register, her stuff cost six times as much as mine. After I came back from Papua New Guinea I couldn't *believe* the way people in Australia spent money. Two Papuans from the mission where I worked came to Australia and visited Mum and Dad. Later they wrote to me: "What a lot you gave up, to come to us. Your family lives in a huge house, with many comfortable chairs and two cars." I wrote back, "Yes, but in that house I have not learnt what I need to know."'

'One's friends,' says Two, 'were band-y, interesting, creative people. That got her into trouble with Dad. Whereas I had boring, stable, middle-class friends, which was approved of.'

'I remember asking and asking,' says Four, 'what the working class was. I mean – *where* was it? As soon as I got the chance I headed down market. I was *desperate* not to be middle class. Even my friends at school were rough as bags. I was smart but I was always in trouble.'

'Two was deeply offended, I think,' says Five, 'when I didn't marry X. She wanted me to marry an American and go and live on Long Island or in Hawaii. That was her fantasy for me. Frangipanis over breakfast for the rest of my life.'

'When Five was having her baby,' says One, 'I suffered for a while from ferocious jealousy. It was mostly displaced on to material things – on to shopping. Mum took her out to Daimaru for a swanky lunch at Paul Bocuse and then bought her a whole lot of fabulous baby clothes. When I heard about it I practically had to stay home in a darkened room for a couple of days. I had terrible memories of staggering home from hospital 23 years ago, with *my* baby, and not even having been given any nappies. And Five's not even *married*.'

AFTERBIRTH

With four sisters, there's one for most moods. Two is brilliant at cooking and gardening. Four is the adventurous one, to go out shopping and dancing with: at a certain point, whenever she and One went out together they witnessed a car crash. Five loves to talk about books and writing, and to compare the nibs of pens. In Three's company, the slightest incident becomes redolent with psychological and spiritual meaning.

Once, Three and One spent a day at One's shack in the bush. The purpose of the outing was to 'sort out some things', to have 'a conversation that was several years overdue'. Reproaches flew both ways. They sat sadly at the wooden table, looking at their hands. Then Three said, 'Want me to wash your face *with a warm washer*?' One recognised the childhood phrase. She presented her face, chin up, eyes squeezed shut, and Three rubbed and wiped, firmly; One could hear her quietly laughing. A little while later, One put some Oil of Ulan on

Three's face. These things seemed very *symbolic*, as did everything else they did up there that day: tearing out the old ivy roots, sawing dead limbs off the shrubbery, making soup for the meal. Then, as they drove away towards the road home, One saw a cow in a paddock with a long red strand hanging out of her mouth. One yelled out, Three stopped the car. The cow had just finished licking the membrane off a new-born calf, which was struggling to its feet. They saw its blunt little head, its coat so matt and clean. The cow set about eating the afterbirth: the thing was clearly a membranous sac; the cow kept licking and chewing at the sloppy mound of it on the grass, dutifully gulping it down. One and Three imagined it already cold, slimy, strandy – it seemed a nauseous duty, and an image of the maternal labours they had been bitterly talking about. Neither of them remarked on this connection, but they sat there in the car, holding the dog by the collar, and watched intently for a long time. Then Three said, 'Oh *look*. All the other cows are coming over to inspect. To celebrate.'

MUSIC

'Once,' says Three, 'I was combing Dad's hair with the comb dipped in Listerine and telling him that I wanted to learn the piano. One said, on her way past, "Be a jazz pianist." And Dad said to her, "Don't tell her what to do."'

'So *you* were the one who made them get a piano,' says One. 'How'd you do it? When I said I wanted to learn the violin they just laughed and made squawking noises.'

'Oh, I pestered and pestered,' says Three. 'And then I set up a stall in the street out the front, to raise the money to buy one. I think I shamed them into it.'

Back in the seventies, when there was such a thing as the three-dollar gig, Four and One used to go out dancing, with all their friends, several nights a week. It would never have occurred to One to imagine herself on stage; but Four watched carefully, then borrowed a saxophone from a man she knew and taught herself a few riffs. Next thing One knew, her sister was up there in a sparkly jacket, playing 'Suffragette City' with a women's band called Flying Tackle.

When Two's daughter decides to leave her medical course and study singing, Two invites Three and One over, one evening, to be a practice audience for the daughter's Conservatorium audition pieces. Three and One jump in the car and rush over there, wearing clean, ironed clothes. They set up the living room like a little stage, and plump themselves on to the sofa in a line, hands folded, chins up, eyes bright. The daughter steps out to sing, sees them eagerly sitting there, and bursts out laughing. She leaves the room, and returns more composed. In the pause before she sings the first note, Two hisses to her sisters, *'Need a tissue?'*

'One came home from university for a visit,' says Three, 'and brought me a Vivaldi record. It was so *exciting* – I'd never heard anything like it before.'

Four is the kind of person to whom it matters how a backing vocal changes, in the bridge of a song, from 'shoop shoo wop bop' to 'bop shoo wop bop'. When she got off the plane at JFK she took a cab straight to Danceteria.

Three can sightread. Three always remembers the words. Three goes to the trouble of making tapes and passing them round the family. Three must have been the only nurse at the Royal Children's in the 1960s who knew Mahler's *Kindertotenlieder*.

'In New York,' says Five, 'I heard some black people singing and playing on the street. I wanted to bawl. I said to the person standing next to me, "Are they from a religion? Show me where to join – I want to sign up." '

At school we were taught to sing in parts. Thus there were years during which we could spontaneously drop into harmony, while washing dishes or on tedious car trips, or very softly in our beds at night when sleep was reluctant to come.

Then we were grownup and nobody sang. Hymns and carols became embarrassing. We wiped 'The Lass of Richmond Hill' and 'The Ash Grove' from our repertoires and went to Europe or got married.

Decades passed. Then Two instigated a Christmas concert. It was fun the first time but soon degenerated into our children miming bad pop records. Anyway when we sang together now we sounded horrible. Our voices had dropped into a lower register and lost their sweetness. None of us could hit the top notes without screeching. We soon gave it up.

But Two secretly persevered, singing along to records of famous chorales. Three played hymns on her piano at night, telling herself she was just practising sightreading. One, at forty, finally found the nerve to take piano lessons. Four, the only one with a serious musical talent and the drive to use it, took singing lessons, practised irritatingly in the car on the freeway, and was soon able to front her own band as a singer instead of just playing saxophone.

'I,' announced Two, 'am going to join a choir.'

She does. And she drags the rest of us into it too, a huge Christmas charity choir with a proper conductor. You pay your $30 and are issued with a score and a practice tape to learn your part from, between rehearsals.

We work hard at it, separately, at home. Our first practice is at Two's place on a Friday evening. We belt out the carols in our terrible harsh (but in tune) voices, then tackle the harder stuff. Just as we roar to the end of the Hallelujah Chorus and close our scores with sighs of triumph, One looks out the window and sees a huge pale full moon rising out of the trees.

When we sing 'The Shepherds' Farewell' from Berlioz' 'The Childhood of Christ', we think privately of our own children leaving us: 'God go with you, God protect you, guide you safely through the wild.' We hope that if we can sing right to the end without crying the music will act as a blessing.

Every Sunday we drive or pedal to the Catholic Hall at the top end of Brunswick Street and sing the afternoon away. All altos now, we are within out physical range. It's important to position ourselves in front of older women, cheerful ones of sixty-plus who come in from their outer-suburban church choirs, who know the works and can sight-sing. We rush each week to get near these guides, the ones with calm, strong, bosomy voices, who won't fade out or get flustered when the timing gets complex, but who lean forward in the tricky bits, to keep us on track.

In a huge choir – 500 or more – a beginner can afford to take risks. You can take wild stabs at the intervals, and your mistakes will be swallowed up in the great rolling tide of sound. We've learnt that in daily life we barely breathe; singing requires an intake and expulsion of air so much more rhythmic and profound that at times we become light-headed and have to grip the seatback for balance.

We are women who have always been fighting our father. Maybe this is why we love the way the men's voices surge under ours, a broad band of deeper sound, something stable and generous that supports the women in their sharper, more fanciful melodiousness. We are astonished by the ability of 500 voices to sing softly, to make a sound like a whisper. We are learning the humility, the modesty, the indispensability of the alto part; accepting the limits and the strengths of maturity.

It's dangerous to look at each other. Two's hanky is always in her hand. If we catch each other's eye, our voices tremble, choke and die. So we are learning to stand beside each other, upper arms touching, looking straight ahead: part of the larger music.

Now that we can sing together, surely none of us will ever die – *surely*?

THE CUCKOO CLOCK

DRUSILLA MODJESKA

1

In my father's house the light is dim. Outside, even on the brightest day, shadows spread outwards from the corners where box hedges and periwinkles meet the yews, and steps dark with moss wind down the hill beneath birches and ash and one glorious copper beech to the alders on the bank and an old jetty where the punt is moored. The children jump onto the punt, one two three four; the big ones catch the little ones, and my father, their grandfather, follows cautious on the bends calling out to take care. The punt is old but still rather beautiful; its wooden slats crumbly and forlorn without the cushions that are kept in the shed. The jetty is slippery and the water dark with silt and vegetable matter. From where we're sitting, above them on the lawn, we hear the children's voices. In the light of a late summer afternoon my sisters lie in deck chairs with a tray of tea things abandoned between them. And although the air is sweet with the scent of catmint and the last of the roses, even there it seems dim to me. I lift my arms as if to push at the sky, and as my sisters turn to ask me what I'm doing, a loud and heavy splash from the river jolts us to our feet. My sisters run to the edge of the lawn. I listen to the silence from the river, a shouting sort of scream, just one, that twists up through the air; then our father's voice. Be careful! Be careful!

We run down the steps, round the corners, through the

periwinkles, past the beech with its copper glories unseen, beneath the alders. On the jetty, the children stand. In the river is Minna, her long coat pulling her down, looking for all the world like a rat. Our father is scrambling along the bank prodding at her with his walking stick, directing her, he says afterwards, towards a muddy beach where the bank has crumbled just before the bend over which the church with its clock tower presides.

On the jetty little Lotty's face is streaked with tears.

'Do dogs drown?' she asks.

'Don't be stupid,' Tom says. 'Everything drowns. Elephants drown.'

'Not fish,' his sister Aggie says.

'Well of course not fish,' Tom says. 'I never said fish.'

'You said everything,' Lotty says.

'Everything on earth,' he says, and takes off to follow Phoebe, my sister, his aunt, who is scrambling along the bank calling to Richard, our father, to be careful. 'There are too many girls in this family,' Tom says. 'Girls, girls, girls.' His hair shines red under the trees. The cuckoo in the nest, the girls call him. That's what Phoebe and I called May. We'd squeeze and squeeze until she fell out, we said. Round and blond and blue, we'd said, how could she be ours?

Standing at the edge of the jetty, I watch the girls, my nieces. Jo and Lotty stand facing the drama on the bank. They are dark, like Phoebe and me. Jo is lanky and awkward with adolescence, Lotty small and compact, but they share the foxy look that comes from us: pointy shoulders, knobbly knees. Between them, sitting on the jetty, is Aggie, exactly the blond that May, her mother, had been at her age, with the same smooth fullness and the same aspect of repose that misled us all into thinking she was as serene as she was lovely, the sort of child of whom people say *she'll break hearts*, with little thought to the friable substance of the child's own heart. But unlike May, Aggie's eyes are an unexpected green. 'Where do they come from?' Tom asks, as if to deflect from the flagrant irregularity of his own unexpected hair.

On the jetty the air flips around us like a landed fish; it flutters and moves, up and down, little eddies of anxiety, a pulse of memory, the lift of loss and anticipation. With the splash, the crash, heard from the lawn, while my sisters leapt to visions of their children tumbling into dark water, it was May that I saw, not falling but floating downwards with only her hair coming up, floating down to the clear gravel at the bottom of the river where we went for picnics. That was a different river, and a long time ago, though I dare say it's still there, and still deep enough for children to swim, with water as bright as crystal bubbling in channels between the weed. We were running ahead; our parents Poppy and Richard were behind us with the baskets; and in front Daisy, May's ancient poodle, mistook for a grassy bank the long soft weed that was growing at the edge and curling onto the surface between us and the chalky channel of the river. In she went, and after her, May. Daisy disappeared into the weed, and then May floated out, her hair blond against green.

'Richard!' Phoebe had shouted, just as she did now, following him along the bank to save another dog, and in he had gone, trousers and everything, and out came May, upside down and streaming; and afterwards Phoebe and I sat chastened by her bed. 'You're our own best sister,' Phoebe said, but there was nothing that could be said to console May, no distraction, no temptation to lift her thoughts from Daisy's sodden body and awful staring eyes. Not even Phoebe's offer of the cuckoo clock. I was the one startled by the offer. May seemed not to notice. 'Truly,' Phoebe said, 'you can have it,' outstripping by far my own contrition that took the silent form of memory: lifting May from her pram, the weight of her body against mine, her little legs pushing and wagging, and while the photographer smoothed my dress, her hand closing around the coral necklace my godmother had given me at the birth of this sister, as if there could ever be any compensation for that first, great interruption, as if it weren't pleasure enough just to lift her up.

And although there was still a year of school terms and holidays before Poppy would go into the sanatorium, the day that Daisy drowned our mother stood on the bank pale with shock as if there was nothing she could do to ward off the spirits that dwelt there, beckoning us into a river she could not save us from. I remember her that day only in absence, no longer the voice that said *hush my darling, hush you now*. That night she slept in with May, and Phoebe was put on a stretcher down with me. 'Look after your little sister,' Richard said when he tucked me in, but no looking after would make Phoebe acquiesce at being away from May and Poppy, banished downstairs where I'd slept since she was born. 'Come on,' I said as she wept in protest, 'I'll make it nice for you.' Even so Richard had had to carry her down. I carried the clock. 'I didn't sleep a wink,' she said in the morning. But it wasn't true. I'd seen her face soften and move, and her hair fan out when she turned, like a little bird with its feathers plumped, while I watched over her and counted down the hours; just as I'd seen her smile when I'd put her in my own bed and told her how Poppy's belly had swollen up with her inside and how I could hear, if I listened very still, a low sort of singing noise.

'I couldn't hear a thing when Tom was inside May,' Aggie says.

'That's because you thought he was a sister,' Jo says. 'You weren't listening for the right sounds.'

The girls press around us on the lawn while in the house Tom helps Richard dry Minna. They want to hear stories from our childhood, they want to know where we all went when Poppy, the grandmother they barely remember, was taken to the hospital. They want to know what happens when families break up. They want to know who pushes who out. Do big

116

sisters push little ones out, or do little sisters grow too big and take up all the room? And they want to know why Phoebe wasn't allowed to take the cuckoo clock when Poppy went to hospital and she and May were sent to stay with the Nortons. They want to know why Richard, their grandfather, our father, couldn't insist, and why he was so upset when the clock was stolen, only a few years ago, from this house which you'd think would be safe enough, up above the river and hidden in the trees. 'Anyway,' Aggie says, wanting a story she's heard many times before, as if the repetition itself will stitch her into the fabric of a family in which strains and separations are part of her woven birthright of love. 'Anyway,' she says, 'seeing as she's the youngest, how come Phoebe had the clock in the first place?'

The cuckoo clock had belonged to Richard's mother Gertie. The case around its time-keeping face was decorated with a gilded pattern of leaves, and flowers with mother of pearl inlay. Above where midnight struck, perched as if to take off in flight, was a bird with its wings marked in burnished copper, and mother of pearl on its neck and chest. No matter how often Phoebe was told that the bird was an eagle, and the clock American, nothing would convince her that it was not a cuckoo, and so the name stuck, even to this day. Gertie's youngest sister, who was a collector of treasures, had been given the clock by a travelling aunt when she was ten, just a year before she died of scarlet fever. After the epidemic was over, Gertie, as the only girl left, inherited the clock. But she never really liked it, Richard said, because it seemed to her a most unequal exchange, a clock in place of a little sister. So when Phoebe came along, clearly the last of Richard and Poppy's brood, (unless there was going to be a son, you wouldn't think there'd be more girls, three was quite enough) Gertie gave Phoebe the clock. In Gertie's mind it meant there'd be no risk it'd replace another real sister; but in Phoebe's mind it meant she could have her own, and that's what the clock became, a surrogate little sister.

But apart from that it was an appropriate gift, for Phoebe, like her great aunt, dead before antibiotics and vaccines, was a collector of treasures. When she was ten, by which time Poppy was home again, Phoebe had her own museum. There was a sign nailed to one of the lime trees on the main road that said *museum*, and an arrow pointing up the hill to our house. There were a lot of jokes and relics and fakes in the museum, like the Tolpuddle Martyrs' hanging rope, Queen Mary's shinbone, a dinosaur's claw, and Lady Jane Grey's scarf, which were treasures of a sort. And there were real treasures like Poppy's Queen Anne teapot lid, grandfather's quill and nibs and the Roman coin one of Mrs Tuck's boys ploughed up in the top field on the hill across the river where Daisy drowned. Not that the coin lasted long. By a very bad piece of luck, the curator of the museum in the town where Richard caught the train to London drove along the road past our village one weekend and seeing the sign *museum*, rather well-painted by May, followed it to the door. He was the only visitor Phoebe ever had other than people who were visiting anyway. Being friends of Richard's, or relatives, her usual visitors were quite willing to pay the penny admission, but the curator told Phoebe, while his children sat in the car and watched, that *there were regulations*. So she let him in for free and, as if it were the only reason he'd come, he pronounced the coin certainly Roman. Phoebe said of course it was, she knew by the markings which she'd looked up in the library. The man said that a coin like that should be in the town's museum, and eventually, after tea in the house and a walk down the garden with Richard while we and the children from the car trailed along behind, the curator took the coin away wrapped in one of Richard's handkerchiefs. When I left home some five years later it was still in the town's museum with a label which read *kindly donated by Miss*

Phoebe Nesbitt, one coin among many in a room full of marked, named and labelled certainties.

It was just as well, May said, that Richard had drawn the line at the cuckoo clock being in the museum out there in the old shed. Richard said it was much too valuable, worth hundreds, and it was to stay inside at least until he got a valuer to look at it.

'What if the valuer takes it off to a museum?' Phoebe asked.

'Of course he won't,' Richard said. 'It's ours.'

'So was the coin,' Phoebe said. 'Mine.'

'We found it,' Richard said. 'It's different. It belongs to the nation.'

'Bugger the nation,' Poppy said, looking straight at Richard which she didn't often those days. 'He was a sour-faced man with those poor miserable children. You shouldn't have given in to him.' She was cross and went indoors. May and I bicycled to the main road and removed the sign. Phoebe went upstairs and took out May's rules for survival which were kept inside the little door at the back of the clock.

'Hands up everyone with a little sister.' Miss Piddington stood at the front of the upstairs classroom with lumpy strands of spittle stretching between her teeth. Up shot my hand, one of the proud ones; but, ignominiously, it had to come down again. Miss Piddington had meant *hands up everyone with a little sister downstairs in the kindergarten classroom*. With five years between May and me, and another year before Phoebe, my little sisters were much too small for that. No use at all. We were never at the same school at the same time. They were, pacing each other, only a year apart, the space between them paced; but whenever they were about to come to school with me, I was moved to another, never to overlap even for a term.

When I hear other people with little sisters talk of the softness, the dizzying sense of love that comes over them when they hear that phrase, *little sister*, when I hear them, these people with greatly loved little sisters, I am sad, as if I never really had the chance. More often pride brought disappointment, as in Miss Piddington's classroom; or love was bound to fear and loss as it was the day Richard rescued May from the bottom of the river. Little sisters brought chaos and unsettled everything. Where once I ruled, now I must serve. I was the one who could carry without spilling, who was old enough to know better. They took over my toys, my clothes, even my bedroom. I was moved out of the room where I'd been snug and safe next to Richard and Poppy, and exiled to a new room they had made for me under the stairs. It was small and narrow and needed the lights on all day. The window was so high I had to stand on a chair to see out. And instead of looking over the garden to Mrs Tuck's cottage and to the road where people walked and cars came rushing down the hill, this window looked out to the orchard where Richard buried Daisy. By the time we left the house there was a host of little crosses, each named and remembered, peeping up from the grass to mark the resting place of white mice, guinea pigs, rabbits, dogs, cats, a tortoise. When the first of the guinea pigs died, the one that was mother to the tribe that grew to forty-six before it was eaten by foxes in a single night, the vicar came to tea, and May wept and wept when he said that animals didn't have souls. She thought they should be the same as heathens and unchristened babies who went to heaven anyway because they hadn't had the chance to know about God. Phoebe said she didn't see why we put crosses for them in that case and she thought she'd be an atheist. The worst fear, the vicar said, was for little girls who had every opportunity to be Christians and wilfully weren't.

'Where do they go?' May asked.

'Really vicar,' Poppy said. 'I think that's quite enough.'

'To horrible hell, of course,' Phoebe said, making a hideous face. 'To frizzle and fry. Where else?'

Phoebe spent a lot of time in her room as a child. May would go up and sit in solidarity under the eiderdown with her. Sometimes I'd go too. I'd read my book and hush them when I got to the bits they liked, Jane Eyre locked away in the red room, and they'd listen as I read, their faces like little oval moons, and it was as if Jane Eyre was in there with us, or us with her, and Phoebe's pretty room as dark as a dungeon. 'Stop,' she'd say when it got to be too much, and she'd look up comforting facts in her encyclopedia. May drew diagrams of complicated transport systems that moved animals and babies and heathens around heaven and earth, as well as between cities and islands and continents. She worked out escape routes, itineraries for journeys we'd make when we grew up.

'Hands up,' Miss Piddington said, 'all those who know what is to be found in Australia.'

'Wheat, sheep and coal,' we chanted.

And witchdoctors who scrape a circle round your skull to cure headaches. May learned that in geography when she was in the upstairs classroom and Phoebe was downstairs in kindergarten.

'I'm not going there,' Phoebe said, grateful all of a sudden for that stuffy downstairs classroom where Little Weed was sick in roll call and everyone else had to go out through the french windows into the pokey garden cordoned off by box hedges the boys jumped over. Miss Piddington, who had never been seen to smile, knew of whole continents where people lived without any of the privileges of the British Empire or the Christian faith. May looked them up in her atlas and marked them on her contingency plan.

'But they don't have water,' Phoebe said. It was Miss Piddington's view that in places where it was very hot there was no water at all. Let alone anything like beech trees or policemen or daily newspapers. And certainly no bottles of government milk growing sour by the boilers.

'There are rivers,' May said, pointing them out. 'And if they're no good, or dried up, we can always dig bores.'

'Even so,' Phoebe said, 'I'm not going.'

In the end, despite May's plans, I was the one to leave. Quickly and definitely. May and Nigel came for a while but their stay was never more than a prolonged sojourn, and the girls still speak of Sydney as they might of a dream. They tell the little ones how you never need lamps except at night and then there are hundreds of twinkling, winking lights, shining in the sky, in the water, even in the trees. They say I can expect them as soon as they finish school. This time it is May who looks sad.

'Is our family to be divided for another generation?' she asks.

'Families are always divided,' I say. 'It's in the nature of them.'

But at that moment, on the lawn where we sit, the air is still and fragrant, and it's hard to remember that there could ever be dissension. Tom comes up with Minna who is dry again, and Richard brings a fresh tray of tea. In the distance we hear the chimes of the church clock strike the half hour.

'I should take a photo,' Richard says, 'while I've got you all together.'

2

Every family has stories; and more often than not these stories take on their own life, detached from anything that might have happened, and become embellished, sharpened, honed for their part in the lives that emerge from their early, almost forgotten origins. In our family many of the stories (fables, histories) revolve around names, definitions, genders, as if, without brothers, without the order of that difference and its accompanying language, we three girls, full of doubts and sensitivities, must always interrogate where we stand.

As well as three daughters, Richard, our father, has three sisters.

'Of course it wasn't a disappointment,' he said when we taxed him. 'I was thrilled to bits with you all.'

'Even with me?' Phoebe, the last born, would ask.

'Especially with you,' he'd say.

But over and over, in a mutual folly, we'd ask, and he'd tell the story of the terrible disappointment of his sister Peg's arrival. Despite the fact that he was ten and already had two other sisters – timid girls who spent most of their time with Gertie, our grandmother, his mother, blocking access to her and generally cluttering up the house – he hadn't noticed the changing shape of Gertie's stomach, or noticing it he had drawn no conclusions that would be of any help to him. So when Aunt Sally, his Aunt Sally, not ours, came into his room at the end of an afternoon of unusual preoccupation among the adults, to tell him there was a wonderful surprise waiting for him downstairs, he naturally assumed that his train set had arrived at last. It must be enormous, he thought, to have taken all day to set up. So he got up from his desk where he had been copying out illustrations of women in complicated medieval dresses, and trotted cheerfully along behind Aunt Sally. On the first landing his father met him with an encouraging squeeze to the shoulder, but just as they should have taken the last flight down to the dining room and the big mahogany table which the train set would have perfectly fitted, Aunt Sally opened the door to his mother's bedroom. A strange place for a huge and elaborate train set, but not impossible, perhaps it would run round the bed and into his father's, our grandfather's, dressing room. One glance into the darkened room was enough to tell him all, and there in the crib was the wonderful surprise of our Aunt Peg. I don't think Richard ever forgave her. And recounting the story as he so often did (on whose instigation? his? ours?) none of us girls believed for a second that we were any more welcome than poor Aunt Peg. He protested. But how were we to believe him on the weekends we drove thirty miles so he could play with Mr Bird's train set, and the story hummed in the air of the car, flapping in through the windows, announcing itself on sign posts, settling into our clothes with the fumes of passing trucks. The car stopped so one or other of us could be sick.

Mr Bird was a solicitor. He and Mrs Bird had three sons and, in the attic of their house, a fleet of tiny trains were set out on a network of rails with stations and bridges, hills and junctions, signal boxes and shunting yards; a whole world of lakes and villages and level crossings. Mr Bird and Richard would disappear into the attic, leaving us downstairs with the spindly, disappointing Bird boys. Poppy and Mrs Bird sat in the kitchen, or out in the sun if it was summer, and shooed us away. Phoebe and I traipsed around the woods on the other side of the road trying to shake off the Bird boys who jostled and twittered around us.

'Why don't you go and play with the trains,' Phoebe would say.

'We don't like them much,' the spindliest of them said. In the house May stood at the bottom of the attic ladder.

'Can I come up,' she asked.

'I'll be down soon, darling,' Richard said.

'Please,' she said.

Driving home Richard beamed satisfaction. 'What a splendid afternoon,' he'd say, while we bickered in the back seat. Who was to sit in the middle, on the hump. Phoebe and I had the best reasons for avoiding it, which meant Poppy intervened and one of us would end up there. Phoebe most likely; that's the penalty of being smallest, last and least important.

'That's enough of that,' Poppy would say to me, and I'd wriggle and slide and with a bit of luck hang onto my seat by the window.

'You'd have preferred us to be boys,' Phoebe wailed as her thin little bottom jolted around on the hump.

'Of course I wouldn't,' Richard said. 'Though I must say I would have loved a train set.'

'For goodness sake,' Poppy said, 'get one anyway. Those boys don't play with it any more than our girls would.'

'I'd play,' May said. 'I'd play every day.'

'Would you darling?' Richard said in one of those voices adults use when children are being cute and they're storing it up for later. 'What a funny girl you are.'

'I would,' she said. 'I really would.'

'There you are Richard,' Poppy said. 'The perfect opportunity.'

But he never did get one, and with only one grandson, though there was talk of it, it wasn't really enough, and nothing came of it. Perhaps he was put off by Tom's preference for cricket, or by May who seems as a mother herself to have inherited Poppy's irritation on the subject. 'That wretched train set,' she says if anyone mentions it, and these days nobody much does.

When Richard married again he married a woman with many sons and few daughters. But although Cecily boasts of their achievements, and new (masculine, rivalrous) stories have joined the family, those step-sons, these step-brothers, are no real threat. It's too late for that, and I'm sure it's true, what Richard says, that now we're here, he quite simply loves us, and the time has passed for thinking about sons and train sets and camping trips and a name handed down. When Richard joins Cecily in singing the boys' praises, and cataloguing their successes – in shipping, hotel management, antiques – we don't believe a word of it. Sometimes we grumble that Richard and Cecily value the conventional – wives, jobs, holiday houses – over the more ambiguous achievements of our lives. But we all know that it wouldn't take much to derail the conversation. In this we have the backing of more girls, Cecily's daughters, and especially Clare, the one most like us, given to extremes, and with a predilection for versions, possibilities and imaginings, who should not be overlooked in any accounting of the family. And even if we've failed on one scale, Richard's girls with not a holiday house between them, it is in us that the hopes have always been carried. Richard's hopes. When Poppy said *never mind, it's only an exam*, Richard said *they must go into the professions*; and was it our mistake, or his, that we thought he meant Phoebe and me, and that the task was split? For it was May, the pretty one (and she was, so pretty, so very pretty) good with children and gentle with animals, who rated, unlike prickly us, as *his lovely girl*. Did he cast these definitions before us? Or did we in our sensitivities take them for ourselves (eagerly, cravenly)? All my life I have heard him on the phone, boasting. 'My daughter,' he says of one or other of us, recounting our doings, our successes, our children, even our jokes, our stories. I hear his voice swell and the deep huffing peal of his laughter. All my life I have listened intently to what he says of them. Them, not me.

'He has no one to hand over to,' I say, conscious of my first-born failures. 'No one to take his name.'

'Don't tell me,' May says, the one of us who would have made the barrister had that been what she wanted. She hasn't forgotten the telegram he sent when Tom was born. *Congratulations for keeping the Grants on the road*, it read. For the girls he sent flowers.

When Poppy went into the sanatorium, May wanted to change her own name. This is another family story: told and told and told again. But Mrs Norton put her foot down. (Enough was enough. She had offered to take one child and had landed two; well they'd cried so and in the end it seemed cruel to separate them. But it wasn't easy. First there was the fuss about Phoebe's clock, but how could she have a fragile thing like that, and valuable too, in the house with all her boys? And then there were Phoebe's corduroy trousers, which in the end Miss Piddington allowed, given the circumstances and the fact that she was a delicate child. The business about the names was the last straw. It wasn't that Mrs Norton was unkind or meant to harm either girl; on the contrary her intentions were the best, but with three children already and not enough help in the house, and Mr Norton away all week, it was a wonder she wasn't in the sanatorium too, even without the addition of two quirky, complicated girls to take care of. Everyone had thought it would only be for a month or two at the most.)

'I won't be any different,' May said, explaining her reasons. 'Only my name.'

'Pretty girls like you,' Mrs Norton said, 'aren't called Fred, and they aren't called Ethelred.'

'You should be grateful,' Miss Piddington said, 'for the name the Good Lord and your parents gave you,' as if there had been high level consultations.

'No,' said Mrs Norton when Phoebe tried in May's place. 'It's not a girl's name.'

'No,' said Miss Piddington. 'And that's an end to it.'

This is a story that is told as a match to Richard's story of Peg and the train set. To other people we tell it for laughs. Within the family, we tell it to make May blush, and to remind Richard that we haven't forgiven him for the deep betrayal of so much as thinking that there might be sons. We tell it as if there were seductiveness in our approach, a story that at once challenges and reclaims our position. We tell it in a lifelong competition for our father's attention; and we tell it to present a united front. It is a story that comes from a time of unreality and disbelief when safety was no longer attached even to the most certain of facts. All these years later we use the worn out humour of an old story as a way of approaching – and controlling – the memory of dark and distant things. For all these reasons it is a story with riders and addendums. It is a story that can never deviate from its proscribed forms, in which we can each have a part.

It wouldn't have been so bad, Phoebe continues, if Woldy hadn't been allowed to change his name from Adrian to Ethelwold, or if he hadn't got the idea from May in the first place. Woldy is still Woldy Norton to this day.

'What happened to him?' I ask.

'I don't know,' May says. 'I never inquire.'

'He lives in Malawi,' Phoebe says.

'Whatever for?'

'He's a trader of some sort,' she says.

May sniffs. 'Don't interrupt,' she says.

And it wouldn't have been so bad if Little Weed hadn't gone on being called Little Weed. She and Phoebe were in the same class. She was youngest of the Toffle children who lived on the edge of a millpond, that's all I remember of them, and that they never drowned. Ben had been in the class above May until he was mercifully dispatched to join the even worse Bill at prep school. Bill and Ben, Little Weed's brothers, were responsible for her name. They said that in any case she was a little weed; and it has to be said that she was, poor child: a snivelly, peaky creature with a crop of stringy yellow hair. No matter how much she wept and begged and pleaded to be called by her real name, Isabella like the Queen of Spain, she remained Little Weed Toffle, even on the front of her class books. This part of the story is allocated to Phoebe.

'I liked her,' May says. 'When she wasn't frightened she could be very funny. She had some good ideas about canals.'

'She was a drip,' Phoebe says.

'That's because you ganged up on her,' May says. 'You were as bad as the boys.'

But no one could be as bad as Bill Toffle. This is my story. Bill, a pale podgy boy with wispy glasses and spiky hair that stuck up into the air, had been in my class at Miss Piddington's and no matter how often she made an example of him in the corner of one classroom after another, nothing could stop his dreadful stories about how girls had their feet tied up in China so they couldn't walk, and bits cut off them in Africa so they couldn't wee, and how babies got poked up into their tummies everywhere.

'What did you want to be a boy for?' I ask May.

'I didn't want to be a boy,' May says. 'You two are the ones obsessed with that, not me. I just wanted a name change, and why not, everything else had changed.'

In the garden Richard stands up and says that as Minna has found herself a warm patch of rug, he'll leave her with us while he goes back to the river. He has finished his tea and is thinking about a ladder from the jetty to the punt. 'We don't want one of you falling in,' he says, surveying his daughters and grand-daughters. Tom is by his side, ready for work. He doesn't need to be asked. But May does.

'Ask your mother to come and give us some advice,' Richard says to Tom.

'I'm settled here,' May says, packing them off, knowing that before long Tom will be back with the same request.

'Please,' he says. 'We're stuck.'

'Oh really,' May says. 'It's only a ladder.'

'To the punt,' Tom says. 'The river keeps rocking us around. We need you.'

Phoebe and I watch May cross the lawn with Tom dancing around her. Her hair as she approaches forty has darkened to the colour of rained-on wheat. She is still slender enough for the silky trousers Richard admires. In her absence the stories stop. For the first time that weekend Phoebe and I open the papers. What I think as I turn the pages, looking but not reading, is that when we tell that story, about Woldy and Little Weed and May not being allowed to change her name, the story we don't tell is that I wasn't there. Banished to boarding school, I've only ever known this story as it comes to me in the retelling. I'm not even sure if I've got the right boy when I tell my bit about Bill Toffle. I didn't know about

Little Weed then, or Woldy. Even in the holidays I didn't go to the Nortons. I went to the Jensens and it's only now when I think of it from Phoebe's point of view that I can see the double betrayal – for in my absence, a useless big sister unable to protect her from anything, and no comfort at all, I took the cuckoo clock. So it would be safe, I seem to remember. Mrs Jensen said of course I should have some things from home; Richard brought them over. This story is never told. Whose idea was it? Mine? Richard's? Phoebe's? The clock was put on the mantelpiece in the room I shared with Henrietta. What happened to it when I went back to school? I don't remember. I don't remember at all. Nothing was in its right place, least of all me. And when I refound it, or found it, a place where I could live, it was a long way from this garden with its trees full of bird calls I can no longer name, from the rivery smells and shadows, from this house with its strange folded-over memories.

Inside I could hear Cecily turn off the radio and call out to Clare who was on her way back to London from the North, here on a short stop, a sudden visit. Clare is our step-sister, the one who least fits Cecily's scheme of things in which there are no muddled identities. The image, glimpsed in whispered stories, of the child Clare sawing the legs off chairs is conveniently erased. It's Richard's girls who are the difficult ones. This is what Cecily says. What we say Cecily says.

The children run to greet Clare; weaving and ducking they take her arms and pull her towards us. Running up the path with them she laughs and they all practise jumping in the air, their voices spiralling upwards as they jostle for her attention.

'So you nearly drowned Minna,' Clare says as she drops into May's empty chair.

We tell her the story in elaborate and orchestrated detail; and she tells us about her week in Yorkshire walking with Luke, her youngest son, and an old lover. When she tells of swimming in the tarn, her description of the evening stillness, the warmth radiating from the rock at the end of the day, provokes in me a lurch of homesickness for my life on the other side of the world's bulge. As I listen to the tumble and roll of her stories with an emotion closer to sorrow than regret, I notice that her boots – scuffed with grass seeds and traces of mud from the banks of streams and lakes – are a German make that is popular in Sydney.

I hardly know Clare. She was a child when I left home, not yet a step-sister. Sometimes I think she is more a sister to Phoebe and to May than I am. It was they who went to parties, tried on hats, shared make-up, crept into X-rated films. I have done none of these things with my sisters. Our present is negotiated through a past that is lived by increasingly threadbare and ancient stories. And even these I make up, for the telling of real stories is too dangerous. There are feelings to be respected, and feelings to be avoided; the question of where the line can be drawn hovers uncomfortably. As it is our lives have taken us in different directions and we have each to bow to our own version of the past. I long to be able to propel this story into a future that glistens as we all look more and more alike, and we take our place as the matriarchs of an ideal family.

As it is, when I think of my sisters I think always of little girls, I think of dress-ups and May clacking along the corridor in Poppy's high heels and Richard's panama hat, a sort of high camp of children's games; of faces pressed to the window as adults came and went; of tea trays laid with cakes on pedestal plates; of dominoes and scrabble and battleships; of the quiet peace of the airing cupboard where the great slatted shelves around the hot water tank housed spare eiderdowns and pillows and left plenty of room for sisters, hunched in winter, whispering, whispering *when I grow up*.

I hardly know Clare, I hardly know her story. And though there are images, handed down in the joint family narrative, along with definitions and descriptions that clatter and clang as they settle this way and that, Clare comes to me fully adult: this woman here, now. A woman who works, who lives in such and such a London suburb, who has two sons, a book-lined flat, and friends who inhabit a world that abuts my own. But May and Phoebe I know from a past in which things that were said about us were given too much weight, and we believed them and carried them into the future, into an adult world that is stripped back again and again to the exclusions and privations of childhood. I want to say this is what they did, my sisters, and swell in pride as I recount their doings: May sailing down the hill on her bicycle and coming to a halt in a graceful curve at the bottom gate; Phoebe walking the length of the garden wall balanced on its narrow top; May playing the *Minuet in G* at Miss Piddington's end of term concert, blushing red with the effort of all those parents; Phoebe with her stories of verve and warriors. But too much gets in the way. I want to say these are my sisters, hear what they have done: this is how they grew up. 'Don't tell my story,' Phoebe says, and I don't: out of fear and appeasement, knowing that nothing I do (or don't do) will ever make up for the fact that I left and left them to it, sealing the separations between us that had begun all those years before.

But for all the distance between us, when I go to their houses I recognise their taste as my own. When May came to my house in Australia she found, without having to ask, the right spoons for soup, the salad servers, the cups that are for tea, the cups for coffee. And in her house I know exactly which Christmas recipe to use for bread sauce and chestnut stuffing. It is as a daring innovation that we buy cranberry sauce. 'What do you suppose we put it in? This?' I ask, taking out Poppy's cut glass and silver jam jar. 'Or this?' A pottery bowl Phoebe brought from Spain. And the girls laugh at us and I think when we're dead and gone these things will be in their cupboards and wonder whether they too will make bread sauce and serve it in the green bowl with the silver sauce spoon? We listen to them in the next room, squabbling; a door slams and the aggrieved sister, May's daughter, my niece, bursts into the kitchen.

'She took my leggings,' she says. 'The grey ones. I was going to wear them. Look. *They're filthy.*'

'Oh dear,' May says. 'Put them through the fast cycle.'

'Is nothing private?' The door slams again.

In families, is nothing private? Too much is private. Too much cannot be spoken. Too much hangs on whose version prevails. And in the swinging surges of childhood and memory, the ownership of stories is never stable, which is why as adults we stick to them so precisely, and why no one dares make the first move into the minefield of their disorder. So I tell the stories they tell, the story of May changing her name and Woldy and Little Weed, and something about it doesn't ring true. Was it Phoebe who wanted to change her name and not May at all? Or was it never true, a story concocted later as a metaphor for the intervention we were unable to make in our fate?

'What made you choose Fred for a name?' I ask May when she comes back from the river and Clare has gone into the house.

'It was short for Ethelred,' she says, and the children all laugh and roll around on the ground beside us.

'I know that,' I say, not laughing, and asking a question that does not belong to the story. 'But why Ethelred?'

'You think it's a joke,' she says.

'At least Ethelwold did something,' I say, 'even if it was only reorganising the monasteries.'

'So what?' she says.

'It was your idea,' I say. 'You could have been Woldy.'

'Ethelred the Unready,' May says. 'I'd say it was fitting.'

'Don't say that,' Jo says, quiet and serious.

'I was a child,' May says, 'thrown out of the nest. I wasn't ready.'

Suddenly it is cold on the lawn. Our chairs, which we have been moving with the sun, are in shadow. May picks up the tray and Aggie follows her towards the house.

'Don't come,' May says. 'I want to see Clare before she leaves.'

So Phoebe and I, alone again, take the girls for a walk. We call Tom but he doesn't want to come. He and Richard are still on the river. We walk across a field of seeded grasses to the woods where the children tell me that last spring while walking with Richard they heard the cuckoo; running ahead they call out the names of herbs and shrubs as if to teach me my own forgotten memories. Autumn crocuses poke up from the earth, a tender pinky mauve, as raw as grubs. At the stile by the wood we turn and wait for Tom who has changed his mind and is running through the grass towards us. The light, slanting now, turns the trees and the grass a yellowy brown, as if England itself is fading at its edges.

'It was cold on the river,' he says. 'Sort of ghosty.'

We smell the damp in the air, a slight odour of rotting vegetable matter. Shivery, we turn back towards the house, and May.

'It's you that upset her,' Phoebe says, taking Lotty's hand in hers, 'not me.'

3

In Sydney I have a friend who's even fairer than May was as a child. She has sky-blue eyes and the loveliest sun-blessed hair. And although she looks nothing like me, there have been times when we've been asked if we're sisters. Perhaps it's our English voices. When we're asked we say yes, in a manner of speaking we are. Like me she grew up in England in exactly the same stratum of that stratified world. Our fathers have friends in common, our schools played matches against each other, but as she is younger than me and in any case neither of us made the team, I didn't see her until she was in Australia: at a party on a roof in Bondi. She was wearing a blue silk shirt that in England would be described as the colour of cornflowers, but that day exactly matched the colour of the ocean. Leaning against the parapet, blue against blue, her face appeared to me as a vision of something I couldn't quite recall. She is the same age as Phoebe, but while Phoebe remains for ever a little sister across an impenetrable rift of experience, Beth and I are of one skin; there's not a sliver of difference between us. When I consider that I've known her for less than ten years I feel a little faint, a vertiginous sense of retrospective disbelief, as if I can no longer imagine the life I lived before, a world without the most perfect of sisters.

Beth has a sister of her own but, as with May and Phoebe and me, their present is hobbled on childhood narratives, ancient rivalries and expulsions. With real sisters friendship must always be struggled for. With Beth nothing is struggled for, and on those few occasions when the cog between us slips, I breathe with the shallowest of breaths and barely sleep until all is restored and the tiny lines around her eyes smooth out again and she tells me her secret jokes as we fly round the corners in her stately car with the blue of the harbour dipping in and out of sight.

May and Phoebe say that while I felt expelled and exiled, they felt abandoned and bereft. They say I left them behind; they say they lost me, their big sister, gone without them. They were stuck at school with the fragments of our parents' marriage waiting for them in the holidays, while I crossed the world to a country where even the moon is upside down. I had a life brimming over with sparkling stories which I sent to them on the backs of postcards of shining harbours and bright reefs. They had drizzle, and guinea pigs to bury, and dogs to drag out of the river. But I say they grew up to each other and with each other. They know their way around streets and lanes that are strange to me; and of the three of us it is they who come closest to being friends. I am an exotic traveller whose return is looked forward to and invariably disappoints.

It is Beth, not May or Phoebe, who understands my exile. It's not that my sisters don't understand being squeezed out; that's the problem, we all understand it far too well. May says I was mean to call her the cuckoo in the nest. I say that in any case I had it round the wrong way, that it isn't the incumbent baby birds who squeeze the cuckoo out; it's the interloping cuckoo dumped there by its mother which pushes the rightful inhabitants out of the nest and lets them crash to the ground with their little wet wings, while she settles in comfortably. She says that's exactly what she means, I'm mean.

'You're impossible,' she says. 'Both of you are. You and Phoebe get everything you want.'

But I say I was the one who crossed the world and must cross it again to be with them. Was that what I wanted? I am the one for whom return is repeated but never complete, so that the grief of exile is felt not in absence, but in the presence of those to whom I cannot be restored. Is that what I wanted?

When I feel their accusation, is it my own guilt that speaks?

'You escaped,' May says.

'I left,' I say.

'So who was the cuckoo then?' the children ask.

'There is no cuckoo,' May says. 'It's just a story.'

'There's a cuckoo clock,' they say, though only two of them are old enough to remember seeing it.

All this Beth knows, and knowing it we need barely speak of it, though it is to her that I turn when the ground slips, just as she turns to me when it happens to her and blood sisters confront each other in their mismatched memories. But at the time, when May, Phoebe and I face each other across the flood plain of our incomprehension, I turn away wounded. It's only to Beth I can say that we represent to each other paths taken and not taken; no wonder it's difficult. May and her children are the family I never made for myself, and there are times when I feel the sharp wind of that absence; there was nothing about me that would *make a lovely wife*, and even if I dreamed of extravagant alternatives, a gypsy foundling, an unrecognised princess (noble resistance), when it came down to it I was as well programmed as May. So I am the one with the career, albeit aberrant and not exactly a profession, that May felt herself discouraged from. And no children. 'But you've done so much,' she says to me when I compare myself and a way of life that from the angle of the happy muddle of her brood can seem austere.

'You never wanted children,' she says. 'Be fair. And think what you've done while I've been doing this.' She gestures. 'Children, children, children.'

'But you wanted us,' the girls say, twirling to remind her of their full glory and wonder.

'I know,' she says, 'but think what else I could have done.'

'Like what?' they ask.

'Like being a designer,' she says.

'Of what?' I say, as if I didn't know.

'Of cities,' the girls chant in voices that seem not to belong to the present. 'Whole cities. Drains, roads, transport systems, everything.'

'Go back to university,' I say. 'You've got the time now.'

'If I do,' she says, 'it won't be for cities. It'll be for ceramics, glazes, firings, wonderful colours.'

'You do that already,' I say.

'More wonderful,' she says. 'More and more wonderful.'

When the clocks were stolen, two months after Lotty was born, it was as if years of fury were unleashed in Phoebe. She was kept awake by the memories provoked by the clock's removal and the child's arrival. The cuckoo clock went and so did Grandfather's bracket clock, Gertie's carriage clock and

Poppy's mahogany clock, a present to me that Richard was minding. They went one afternoon during a week when Cecily was in London with the youngest of her sons, back from the Middle East and set up in one of his hotel suites. Richard came home earlier than expected and found the front door bolted from the inside. By the time he had walked round to the kitchen door which was unaccountably open, and the penny had dropped, it was too late. The front door was open, the clocks had gone and so had the car he'd noticed in the lane behind the garage. A professional job, the police said, the Commissioner himself rang, and despite the spectacles that had been dropped in haste, and circulars to all dealers in clocks, there has never been a trace either of the thief or the clocks. Richard seemed to grow older with their disappearance, his limp got worse and his hair turned a whiter white.

'That clock,' he said, 'had history in it. It was my mother's.'

'It was mine,' Phoebe says, and Richard flinches. 'The one thing that was really mine.'

A year later, when I was visiting for Christmas, I was sure I saw the cuckoo clock in a shop in Camden Passage but Phoebe said it was nothing like it, nothing at all, couldn't I even remember that, and now she'd dragged all the way across London with a baby, why didn't I get my facts straight, all I ever did was tell stories to suit myself. In the face of the wrath of a younger sister one hangs one's head. There is nothing else to do. She says she remembers me reading my book in the front seat of the car, in Poppy's seat, while Richard took her screaming into the Nortons. She says she remembers being left with Gertie in that dark and gloomy house that smelled of porridge and old men, while I went to London on the train with Aunt Peg. She remembers how I showed off my new dresses, making twirls for Richard to admire, while she knew that one day they'd come down to her, a hem and a collar turned, by which time no one would be the least bit interested, even Richard. But my memories of her aren't like that. They're of an elfin child who could take any part in a play and breathe life and humour into it, a little girl in a robe taking her bows on the lawn and all the adults lined up in deck chairs clapping and laughing; they're of a museum crammed with labels and diagrams and morsels and tit-bits of life taken from history and family and neighbourhood, woven into a storehouse of gems; a girl on a pony riding down to the gate for the mail, and news of scholarships and all kinds of possibilities; a bridesmaid handing me roses. These are the things I remember. These and the hair pullings and the tantrums and the door slammings. Hers, and mine. All of ours.

When at last Beth met Phoebe, I feared I would be wrecked on the shoals of my own disloyalty.

'For goodness sake,' Beth said. 'I know everything about her. Surely I can meet her.'

But that is the point. I'd told too much, and too much as a complaint, even to Beth, and Phoebe is after all my little sister and deserves my protection. She is right, I'd given her little enough as a child, and before she'd even left school I was up and off to the other side of the world and far too proud ever to let on how hard it was, banished to a world without sisters. It was a long time before I found Beth.

Phoebe, Beth and I met at an Indian vegetarian restaurant in Soho. 'I've asked Clare to join us,' Phoebe said as we settled into our seats. And we all smiled as the door opened and Clare came in with her wild shock of hair, so unlike her sisters-in-laws' county smoothness. *Through a hedge backwards*, Cecily says. *Lovely*, Phoebe says. Beth recognised her at once, though she'd never made the connection, a friend of a friend from school. Clare, Phoebe and Beth were all in the same year at their various schools. They recognised each other not through that, but through everything that had happened since. Five years older, by the old set of rules, I should have been the outsider, but in that restaurant those rules no longer applied.

We were four women lunching together in a restaurant in London at the end of the twentieth century. To hear us speak, to see us even, no one would have guessed the complications that bound us as sisters, or not. It wasn't until the very end that we spoke of family, and then fleetingly and in passing; I still didn't feel quite able to ask about the child Clare who sawed the legs off the nursery chair on Boxing Day the year Cecily and her father separated. For all her stories, for all her ease, something about her does not invite confidences, and there's always the possibility it wasn't true. Perhaps Phoebe has asked, but if she has it's a story she keeps to herself.

Outside in the street we embraced warmly: Clare and me, then Phoebe and me, Phoebe said how pleased she was to have me there, and although I felt it too, that unaccountable and ancient affection, it was with Beth that I felt the affinity as we stood in the weepy damp of post-imperial London. We watched for a moment as Phoebe and Clare set off, back towards Clare's office and Phoebe's tube. Then we turned in the other direction, winding our way past bookshops and arcades, trying on this and exclaiming over that, talking all the time of other things, other places, other people, until we reached her favourite patisserie and I remembered the finely textured feel of a life that in England is overshadowed by the demands of the past that sisters specialise in.

Phoebe says I was mean to both of them. To her and to May. She says I used to make them go and read their books behind the barn so they'd be out of the way and not come back until lunchtime. I don't remember this at all.

'Surely I didn't,' I say.

'You did! You did!' May and Phoebe chorus, and the nieces try it on Tom but he won't go.

'Why did you let her?' they say.

And so do I. 'Why did you?' I say. 'I couldn't have forced you.'

But they never answer. Everything stops with the story, the

same story, the same stories told over. The stories of children, six, seven and twelve, whose mother went away to the sanatorium: suddenly and without warning. May is wrong when she says there was no cuckoo; it'd be nearer the mark to say there was no nest. We all fell out, one two three, and it must have seemed that I, the eldest, the one to whom they turned, failed them, whisked away in the other direction on the train that'd take me to school, and a still-impossible future. That I too was unready is no defence. Nor is it a cause for guilt. Survival exacts its price.

That evening at Richard's when we'd all returned to the house and the smaller children had had their baths, we sat down to dinner at the table that had once been in our grandfather's house; the table on which Richard's train set was never laid out. For all those years of our growing up, as grainy as the black and white photographs that prevent us from forgetting, we'd take our places at that table under Gertie's gaze and the name of the family. Now it's only Cecily who has our father's name. The rest of us are on travelling names that in his company take us in two directions at once – drawing us back towards him as certainly as they propel us into the future of our other selves.

As if it were a celebration, Richard opened champagne; but the mood was not festive. May said she was tired and went to bed as soon as she'd finished her coffee. Phoebe bickered with Cecily about the Duchess of York. Richard questioned Jo about her 'O' level syllabus and asked Aggie which grade she had reached with the piano. He asked Jo if she'd thought of the law as a career and looked doubtful when Aggie said she wanted to play in a band not an orchestra. Phoebe was sharp with him, and perhaps it was for this reason – a family's resistance to definitions that no one holds to any more – that he replied as he did to Tom's question. Right at the end of the meal, as Cecily was about to clear, Tom asked his grandfather, our father, what he'd have liked to have been had he not been a barrister.

'I'd have been a designer,' he said.

'What of?' Tom asked.

'Well,' he said, 'I sometimes think that what I'd really have liked would have been to design ladies' dresses.'

Phoebe knocked her glass over in shock.

'Richard!' she said over the children's shrieks, 'you're teasing us.' She is certain that he was (*the sod*, she says) but though it seems unlikely as a desire for the father we know, I'm not so sure; and this now seems set to join the repertoire of funny stories that keep the family past from spilling over into less manageable emotions.

'What sort of ladies' dresses?' Tom asked. 'What would you have made them of?'

'Silk,' Richard said. 'Taffeta. A little bit of satin. That gauzy stuff.'

'Chiffon,' Cecily said. 'I've never heard such nonsense. It must be the effect of having all the girls here.'

She stood up and started collecting the plates. She didn't like the joke, but it showed no signs of abating. The children were milling around; I left them to help and went up to May's room. She was reading in bed. I told her what had happened, about Richard and the dresses, and neither of us laughed.

'I suppose it wasn't possible,' she said, 'what with the war and everything.'

'And all of us,' I said.

'We shouldn't let it become a story,' she said. 'We should stop all these stories. They get me down.'

'But how?' I said. 'How?'

The next morning, after a night in which the ghosts of ancient possibilities conspired against sleep, and doubt chipped at the grooves in which memory is held, I rang Beth long distance to Australia.

'Is it sunny and bright?' I asked.

'No, silly, it's night.' she said. 'When are you coming back?'

Downstairs in the hall I could hear May and Phoebe stack the bags and organise the children for the long drive home. I heard them run up and down the stairs. I heard voices raised in farewell and the garden door bang as Cecily set off into the village in her Monday clothes. I heard Richard calling up for me. I waited for the click on the line as Beth hung up; treading slowly, pausing stair by stair as if to draw in my too sharp edges, I rejoined my family. There are hugs for the children and pound coins all round while Richard, our father, their grandfather, lined them up, one two three four; and the three of us, too old to be organised, walked to the garage with our arms around each other, a united presence seen by anyone walking past, *Richard's daughters, those girls together again*, exchanging promises and regrets, quick fluttery kisses.

When May and Phoebe had filled the cars with their respective children and had revved sour fumes into the damp river air, and we had all waved goodbye, Richard and I watched them disappear towards the bridge and the road that would take them to the motorway: one car turning north, the other turning south. Instead of walking back to the house as I had expected, ready to put on the kettle for a cup of tea before my train, Richard turned to me and asked quite formally, if, as eldest daughter, I'd accompany him to the church. 'Of course,' I said, although for some reason, as if I already knew what he had to say, the request filled me with an anxiety as deep and familiar as a blush. So we walked into the village together, and climbed the steep stone steps to the church which looks out over the river at the bend just beyond the jetty. Across the river the houses of the village sat squat and square. Beyond them, small fields, low hedges, and in the distance a ridge that was once a Roman fortification.

'This is where I want to be buried,' Richard said, and pushing open the curved doors at the end of the dark nave so that we could see the watery glitter of river and sky, he told me again the terms of his will. But this time there was a rider. In addition to a straightforward division, would go his desk and bookcases to me, and to May the punt and the leather globe from his study. While the clock struck the hour we stood in the doorway like an illustration in a Victorian novel: father and daughter in thin sunlight.

'And if it's all right with you,' he said taking his gold watch from his pocket and holding it out by its chain, 'I'd like to leave this for Phoebe.'

I reached out to look at the watch I have seen so often, and the chain that has rested for as long as I can remember across my father's heart. It lay like a flattened orb in my hand, heavy and delicate, with the front that opens and the ornate initials of my great-grandfather.

'She'd like that,' I said.

At the top of the steps we hesitated and turned towards the river as though we were both reluctant to leave its assured flow, to make the transition through so fleeting a present from the distant land of the past to the future that separates us; a future in which I could no longer deny that the day would come when the three of us, Richard's daughters, would stand there at the church above the river without him, our beloved father: the one who draws us together even as we move apart, and gives meaning to our lives as sisters. What stories will we tell each other then, when he is gone? What stories will there be? Below us on the bank the ash, unconcerned by such thoughts, quivered on their long stems, a silvery green that seemed in that watery light to be composed more of movement than of colour.

THE DARKLING SISTERS

DOROTHY HEWETT

In the 1920s two awkward young women are standing in front of a Victorian terrace wearing identical short pleated dresses that show their art silk knees. Their eyes are shaded beneath black fringes, satin helmet hats and Japanese sunshades. The light is bad but staring into the camera lens there is a look they both share, an indefinable air of unbearable sadness and dislocation. They are obviously sisters.

It is 1993 and that terrace in Jersey Road, Woollahra, doesn't exist any more. Transformed by a high iron grille security fence and a fake Italianate facade it would be a most unsuitable background for the ungainly sisters. That's one way to confuse the ghosts. If they can't recognize the place they might stay away forever.

But in 1974 when we first saw it, with the auction sign out front, the house was neglected, overgrown, the cement in the courtyard cracked, the cast-iron balcony peeling. At the bottom of the stairs there is an icy place where something unspeakable must have happened. In the front room a strip of shabby plum-coloured carpet is worn thin in a white ring. Who walked there night after night describing that sinister circle? In the cabinet of an ancient console gramophone propped up in a corner there are a few cracked 78s – Marche Militaire, the Missouri Waltz, Tea for Two, The Merry Widow medley. And suddenly I see it. A single bed in the middle of the room with an old fashioned lightpull rigged up over it – and all night long for years and years the footsteps of some haunted somnambulist have gone round and round the bed till the dark red pile turned white with sorrow.

In the back room there is an even more disturbing atmosphere. The air seems to push against the door and the window with a kind of frantic urgency. The shed in the tiny back yard is sunk under an unutterable gloom. In the attic on the third floor something thickens and hums.

And yet the house with its delicate wooden fretwork, plaster ceiling roses, pink marbled fireplaces and curving staircases has such charm. All old houses have ghosts. Painted and recarpeted, with the back shed pulled down and the kitchen and bathroom renovated, it will be ideal. We bought it at auction the next day. We never saw the owner. The estate agent told us she was a very old lady who, with no family left after her sister died, had gone into a retirement home.

And then began such a period of demolition, of falling plaster, dangling electric wires, ripped out floorboards and plumbing, such a transformation with paint and wallpaper, such additions and renovations that we had no time to waste on ghosts. When the plaster and lath ceiling fell with a thump on our brass bedstead seconds after we'd vacated it, there was a moment of disquiet, but surely such accidents happen regularly in the renovation of Victorian terraces.

When we discovered the sepia photograph of two awkward long-chinned young women, hidden under the lino amongst the mildewed *Herald*s, we propped them up on the marble mantelpiece. Posed under oiled paper sunshades in waistless fuji, helmet hats pulled down to their eyebrows, they stood in front of the house, unsmiling, with the touching melancholy of the past. If, sometimes coming into the sitting room towards evening, I heard a whisper of fingers closing the wooden shutters, caught a whiff of Palme Violetta or Cashmere Bouquet, surely they seemed benign enough to live with.

Lined with bookcases, furnished with desk, typewriter and filing cabinets, the back room became my study. Sitting staring out the window for inspiration, I often felt as if a hand placed on my shoulder was inexorably turning me back into the shadows, but I chose to ignore it. My view was only the rotary clothesline and the shed cut in half for a laundry. If I imagined that it screamed I kept it to myself.

The children, sharing the attic with a huge green cardboard crocodile, seem unaware of ghosts. In her last year at primary school our youngest daughter plays Mrs Pankhurst in 'Oh, What a Lovely War'. Haranguing the audience beneath a large black picture hat, she looks like a passionate mushroom. Her older sister wears see-through Indian muslin, sings like a bird, and wags it from Sydney Girls. Her favourite music is country and western; her favourite singer, Bonnie Raitt.

There is something almost pastoral about Jersey Road. With its rows of Victorian terraces built without damp-courses, tarted up with plastic paint and pots of cumquats, it is a good address. When I give the name, the faces of shopkeepers and taxidrivers break open in obsequious smiles.

In the early mornings, amongst the statues of Diana, Hercules and Henry Parkes, my husband walks our old dog in Centennial Park to chase the ducks and tree imaginary possums. 'Do you notice anything funny about this house?' I ask him. 'It's like a chook pen,' he grumbles, but when I look up he is standing out in the street photographing the renovations. I send the photographs to my sister in Western Australia. A research doctor for the Cancer Council, she has settled down with her husband and children in our grandparents' old house with the jarrah verandahs looking out over the Swan River.

'It's lovely,' she writes back, 'just the sort of place I've always imagined for you. I can't wait to see it.'

She has always told me a writer needs peace, quiet and protection, and I have usually listened (particularly on medical matters). 'My sister says' is a running joke in our family.

But who is fingering the locks, who is playing hide and seek behind the wooden shutters, who waits in a path of shadow at the foot of the stairs, whose footsteps shuffle lightly under the rose arbour? Is it the two young women in the sepia photograph or only the drunks, the madmen and the poets arriving at 2 a.m. to play their endless tapes of Bob Dylan and Billie Holliday?

The old Scottish lady who lives next door sips tea from my grandmother's china in the front courtyard.

'Those sisters who lived here before you, they were nice old things, devoted, never apart. When one died the other pined. She used to come out in an old fashioned hat and overcoat, dressed for town. She was waiting, she said. "Waiting for who?" they asked her but she couldn't tell them so they took her away.'

'Did you know them well?' I ask her.

'The sisters? Not well. They kept to themselves but I always knew they were ladies. Breeding tells,' she says.

When Old Tom streels up the road from the pub, knocking over the bikes in his front yard, she winces, patting her turrets of white hair into place.

'My landlord's a terrible man, steals my mail, thumps on the floor all night, and the language. It's not what I'm used to, but beggars can't be choosers. My husband lost a fortune before he died. We were in the antique trade in Edinburgh. And every Christmas when the tree was lit we'd open the windows of our bluestone mansion and wait for Madame Nightingale. Veiled, dressed all in black, she'd sing carols for us out in the garden under the falling snow. Afterwards she'd come to the door for her fee. Disfigured for life, a former opera star, beautiful until her lover's wife threw acid into her face.'

'But the sisters?' I persevere, pouring another cup, 'what about the devoted sisters?'

'Oh! the sisters,' she says, vaguely sipping. 'They're dead and gone my dear, and we don't speak ill of the dead.'

Smoothing her best silk over her knees, she goes back to her upstairs bedsit with the Early Kooka leaking gas out onto the balcony. The Curtsy Man trots by on his way to the corner shop bowing and flirting his fan. My smallest daughter bows back to him and smiles. 'He's sweet,' she says.

In the tiny park littered with dog turds a sad man exposes himself as she goes past. On the corner opposite, fashion photographers drape their models against a crumbling sandstone wall. Under the street lamp at midnight, quarrelling couples enact their bitter departures.

In the mild twilights, sitting out in the courtyard amongst the bulbuls and the black velvet butterflies, watching the Curtsy Man pass by, it seems that even the sepia ghosts on the mantelpiece are laid. And if at the bottom of it all there is a certain disquiet, if the harmony of our lives is in some subtle way disrupted, how can it be otherwise with such a welter of new faces, such a turmoil of new experiences, such a medley of flattering voices? We have become an institution, but the house can hardly be blamed for that, and what is there to blame it for anyway? Isn't this why we came from distant Western Australia, to find the mecca, to write plays, poetry, and stories, attend opening nights at the Opera House, experience the great city, become famous. So having done all that, what has gone wrong? There are nights when the house is racked with noise, when pushing my way into the kitchen crammed with bodies, somebody asks me, 'Who are you?' and I answer wryly, 'I live here.' But do I? Who lives in this house on Jersey Road? Who orchestrates the myriad lives that move in and out of these doors, or are we just an anarchic mob running out of control, like a herd of swine on a sandstone cliff face? In these rooms full of sound I seem to have lost touch with everyone. My husband and my children move like ghosts through my life. When old friends call, they stand uneasily at the entrance staring in at the zoo.

'We can't come to your house any more,' they say, 'we can't

talk to you. There are always too many strangers.'

And who are these strangers who both fascinate and repel me so that, falling in love with their endless self-centred chatter, I challenge my growing daughters for their attention? Caught in an intrigue in the chill space at the bottom of the stairs I listen spellbound to the murmured confidences. I am always listening, for underneath there are other voices I can never quite identify.

Sometimes I panic. I think if I run away, change my name, live in a quiet house somewhere in the country with empty sunlit rooms, we can start again where nobody knows us. When we were children, on rainy days my sister and I used to build cardhouses on the sitting room carpet. Outside in the drenched paddocks the sheep moved in steaming flocks, the crows cawed overhead, but inside the farmhouse we were safe and warm, building our flimsy structures. In the middle of each cardhouse there was a space flooded with light. I wanted to crawl inside that secret room, and be enclosed there forever. Instead, years later it will become Nada, nothingness, 'the clean well lighted place' in the Hemingway story about the two waiters in the Spanish café. Later still I will use it as the central image in my own autobiography.

But what were we really building long ago in the rainy light on the sitting-room carpet – some small bright enclosed self that could never be violated? In those first years we lived a life of such extraordinary closeness, hidden from the world of grown-ups as if we were the only subscribers to a secret society limited to two. That early bonding set up such indivisible links between us that when we were teenagers coming into a room full of strangers we'd seek each other out with our eyes and smile with secret understanding.

'Why is everyone so dumb except us?' We'd laugh conspiratorially with an overriding egotism. Perhaps that was all we had in common, that extraordinary self confidence. We believed we could do anything. Two girls, in that time and place, where did it come from? We were so different, you and I, Janus-faced, like the two sides of a coin. You with your dark hair, olive skin and hazel eyes, your calm judicious manner. Me, fair-headed, blue-eyed, furiously emotional. You took two degrees in psychology and medicine and became a counsellor for the dying. I became a writer.

'Do you always think of me as your little sister?' you ask me.

Of course, ever since I handed you my new Christmas doll because you cried for it. She was a big creamy doll with long black glistening hair and blue eyes that opened and shut between spiky eyelashes. When you dropped her she shattered into a dozen china pieces but I didn't cry.

'I shouldn't have given it to her,' I said, and was briefly enshrined in the family mythology as the reasonable angel. When did all that change? When did you usurp my position? When did I become the wayward, irresponsible, reckless daughter and so, by definition, the youngest? One day you stopped being 'the little sister' and became the good, the level-headed reasonable one, but when did we assume these roles? Certainly not in childhood when I was always the benevolent dictator of our small universe; but maybe not so benevolent after all, just bossy. When was I deposed? Was this reversal imposed on us from above or did we embrace it for our own convenience? My husband says I collaborated deliberately, playing God's fool for the family while they sat around raising their collective eyes to heaven, enjoying the show. An empowerment by anarchy. It probably gave me room, let me find my own space.

Remember that April Fools' Day when I dressed up as a tramp in our grandfather's old clothes? I hid my long hair under his old felt hat and sent you in to tell them there was a stranger pinching eggs in the chook house. When our grandmother came out shouting and threw the washing-up water over me, I ran away into the creek bed. My mother panicked, 'Get the kids in.' She was out on the verandah shading her eyes, calling and calling. 'Where's your sister?' she asked you. 'I haven't seen her all afternoon.' But you said nothing. It was the Depression, the time of the swaggies on the roads, the haves' fear of the have-nots. When the men came in from the paddocks the women were full of it. 'He's been circling the house for hours.'

'It's a funny thing,' said my grandfather, 'but the dogs aren't barking.'

My father started to run. He could run fast. He was once a place-getter in the Stawell Gift. 'Stop,' he called, 'stop. What do you want? Who the hell are you?' His voice sounded angry. The joke had gone far enough.

When I sat down on the old plough and pulled off my grandfather's hat, my hair came cascading down to my shoulders. 'Hullo, Daddy,' I said, 'April Fools' Day.'

They never stopped marvelling over it.

'First I thought it was a dwarf,' my father tells them, 'but then I saw the little hands sticking out of the rolled-up sleeves and I said to myself, "No, it's an idiot boy."'

Sometimes when we went to the Saturday matinees at the Plaza or the Piccadilly, I'd sit on the bottom of the 'circle' steps crossing my eyes, letting my mouth hang open, pretending to be your idiot sister while the passers-by stared. Why was I always playing the Zany and why did we giggle about it so uncontrollably afterwards? In all our games you were the perfect collaborator. Our mother was obsessed by your 'darkness'. Before she married our father she was warned there was 'dark blood' in his family and it played on her mind. The 'dark blood' turned out to be a legacy from our Jewish great-grandmother, but there is an old photograph of you as a child perched barefoot in the almond tree. In your brown velvet dress with the lace collar you look like a gypsy. That was how you went to the RSL Fancy Dress Ball, dressed as a gypsy. I was a fairy in spangles and wire wings with a silver cardboard star in my hair.

Looking back I have remembered the exact moment when our relationship altered. It is 1947 and you are stepping off the Trans-train after your journey across the desert. The two years in Sydney have changed you. You went a plump round-faced girl. You have come back a stylish young woman dressed in a modish grey flannel suit with the latest long skirt that nobody in Perth has seen before. You have cut your hair, and against the new thin planes of your face, a small soft felt toque is tightly fitted into your cheekbones. On your feet are marvellous grey suede shoes with high heels and silky buckles. You have such mystery, such allure, for the first time I feel inferior, frumpish and matronly, with my heavy milky breasts and my first baby pulling down my arms. Staring at you on the station platform I feel such resentment and envy. You are so completely yourself, undivided by parturition and the burden of motherhood. It is as if we stand on the same square of earth but inhabit different planets, you on one side, me on the other, shut out forever from your starry dark complete-ness. Standing there on Perth railway station with our parents beside me, the three of us so dowdy and provincial, I watch your eyes, flecked green under the close-fitting hat, and know you will never be 'my little sister' again.

Even our mother seems bemused. At fifty-one she has taken to wearing gunmetal stockings and navy blue dustcoats to hide her thickening figure.

An only child, unloved by her mother, idolised by her father, she has never had to face the problems of sisters, but she did have two young maiden aunts who made her their surrogate child. Eva was plain, snub-nosed and stylish. Dora was sweet-faced and delicate with gold-rimmed glasses. They painted, rather badly, on glass and canvas; bouquets of flowers, waterfalls, Highland cattle, copies of Edward Landseer. Eva had tantrums and took turns. She wrestled the brush out of Dora's hand and deliberately painted 'The Stag At Bay' with a crooked leg. She was jealous. She wanted our mother to herself. When Dora died of TB in the sanatorium, Eva felt sad and guilty, but nothing changed. In the family archives Dora was canonised. She'd given up her fiancé, boiled her eating utensils, kept her crockery separate and always refused to be kissed. She never spread her germs. Eva, earthbound, culpable, was condemned to live. She only gave up her lover because he was common and dropped his aitches. Her reward was not in heaven but to be an unpaid servant for life in her brother's house. When she went mad they put her away in a 'home' where soiled old women sat rocking and weeping on the dunny seat for hours. When she shouted they gave her shock treatment. She wasn't allowed to have her own silk stockings. All her life she was punished for Dora. Sometimes when we took her for a drive she'd try to jump out of the moving car, until my mother called out sharply, 'Behave yourself, Auntie.' It was a far cry from those long-ago mornings when we climbed into her bed, pulling out her grey hairs while she recited 'King Bruce and the Spider'.

Casting me once again as the family fool, who can't be trusted with money, my mother cuts me out of her will.

'She'll be all right,' she says, 'you can give her something when she needs it.'

'If you do that,' my sister tells her, 'I'll have to divide the estate and it will cost a fortune in gift duties.' I inherit the family home with all its contents. Every night after work we sift through the things an old woman keeps: bottles of pills and buttons, false teeth that never fitted, faded letters, packets of seed, scuffed baby shoes and locks of hair, birth, marriage and death certificates, laddered stockings, the keys to forgotten doors, old photograph albums.

And there we are, the seven ages of woman; fat naked babies displayed on velvet cushions, little girls in smocked shifts with kookaburra brooches, panama-hatted schoolgirls, teenagers posed like bathing beauties in Speedo swimsuits, young women in emerald taffeta and flame georgette with diamanté shoulder straps, young mothers clasping babies against gathered skirts and cotton blouses, menopausal matrons in slack-suits and synthetic shirts with floppy bows to soften the neckline. I am always two-and-a-half years older – a little taller, a little ahead, with the first makeup, the first evening dress, the first husband, the first babies, until finally the gap closes and we are two middle-aged women with grown-up families. But there is always that subtle difference. In these old snapshots I am always a little apart, the maverick who comes and goes, who won't stay put, who refuses to fit in. In the final analysis I can't really be trusted. The husbands who accompany me keep changing their faces and my children have different genes.

'You'd better take the family photographs,' my sister says, 'because you're the eldest.'

Overnight my status has changed. Not by natural authority but by a benign gift from my younger sister, I have not only inherited the family home but have become custodian of the family history. What was mine by right has been bestowed upon me. I have been enfolded into these generations of hoarders, have sworn to be different and turned out just the same.

So you see I know about sisters, but what about the two little blonde sisters asleep in the top of the house? What do I know about them? Cold-hearted young men play us off one against the other. How hard it is to abdicate before all that nubile beauty, but beneath it the loyalty survives, the strange underground familial allegiance, the female knowingness that mothers and daughters share with sisters.

What happened, I wonder, between the ghostly sisters? Was it hate or love or both in this unquiet place? Who owned the house? Who slept in my study? What happened at the foot of the stairs? Who walked in a ring night after night round the bed? The old lady from Edinburgh says they were sweet old things, devoted. When one died the other was grief-stricken, but is it true? Why did the one who was left behind put on her hat and coat and wait in the courtyard? Where was she going, who was she waiting for? I'll ask at the corner store. Jack's grown up in this street, lived on top of the shop with his mother, then took it over when she died. He's sixtyish now, knows everyone, likes a good gossip.

'Jack, who owned the house before us?'

'Two old maid sisters. Lived there for umpteen years.'

'What were they like?'

His glasses gleam in the light. 'Better not say. It's got a dark history, that house.'

'Weren't they sweet old things, devoted?'

'Sweet old things!' he snorts. 'Barmy, the two of 'em, but she should have been reported. I would have done it meself but I was too young.'

'Reported for what?'

'The way she treated 'er, the young one, bit simple, a giggler, mad on the men.' His voice grows softer. He weighs and wraps in a dream. 'But there was no cause to keep her locked up in her bedroom day and night. You could hear her crying from the lane. I stood on a fruit box once and looked through the window, saw her sitting there sobbing, her hair all over her face. She beckoned and called and showed 'er knickers but I ran away.' Portentous with secrets, he leans across the counter. 'That winter she was locked out in the shed, freezing cold with snow on the mountains, you could hear her coughing and wheezing. She died out there of pneumonia.'

'And the other one?'

'Oh, she lived on in the house, had it all to herself now, had what she wanted, didn't she? But her conscience was bad. She'd come out into the front yard with an old satin hat and a moth-eaten monkey hair coat on, trying to leave, trying to get away. She did look a guy. "They're coming for me, Jack," she'd say. They come all right, took her off to the loony bin where her brother had gone before her. Maybe she was lucky at that, the younger one, dying.'

'What were their names?'

'They were the Darkling sisters, Eleanor, Milly. Mother knew them when they were young. Sullen, never mixed, she said. There was a younger brother they had to take care of, finished up out at the funny farm. Have you got all you wanted?'

And here they come now, Eleanor and Milly. Brows fierce and sullen under their satin helmets, they are dragging a little boy by the hand. Dressed in an old-fashioned sailor suit, he whines and walks awkwardly, his fat knees rubbing together. He has pissed his pants.

I go back to the house. It looks closed in on itself, deserted. In late autumn the evenings come down early. The bamboo is rustling by the front fence, the currawong flies over calling harshly on its way to the park. There are no visitors. The girls will be out all night at a pyjama party. My husband is away on the south coast writing his book in a hut in a spotted gum forest. Before he left, he took the old dog, incontinent, crippled up with arthritis, and had him put down. I step onto the verandah. Between the shutters and the glass there is a fumbling, a whisper. Is it the wind? In that room beyond, Eleanor paced round the bed with her guilty conscience, in the next room Millie sobbed and shook at the door handle. In the shed outside in the yard she died. What happened at the foot of the stairs? What happened in the attic? Did Millie flirt in the hallway with her silly childish giggle, did she steal Eleanor's boyfriends, spoil her chances of marriage? Was she surprised in the attic with her skirt up round her waist? They are whispering now, they are giggling and stumbling, they are showing themselves, two sisters, Eleanor, Millie, entwined in

the corners, arm in arm, before it all happened. I put out my
hand but they ignore me. With a swish of their silken skirts
and a dusting of Coty's face powder they have gone through
the french doors, dissolved into the garden. The Curtsy Man,
flirting his fan, bows to them as he passes or is he only bowing
to me? I run out after them but they have already disappeared,
passing like smoke, only the tap of their dyed satin shoes
echoes between the street trees. How can I stay in these rooms
thick with their presence? If I ring my sister tonight, will she
come? This beautiful house, she'll say, and you've spent so
much money, how can you bear to leave it? In a day or two
she'll be here, mending my torn dresses, telling me not to be
fanciful. We'll look at each other over the heads in the
crowded rooms and smile. Before she leaves she'll buy me a
china teapot in Queen Street. A week after she's gone the gold
lid will shatter to pieces under the kitchen tap.

I wake early in the morning and lie still, listening. 'Velia'
is playing, very faintly and scratchily, downstairs. I am
curious. Who has repaired the old gramophone and who is
playing it at this hour of the morning? Have the girls come
home early? I get up in my nightgown and move to the landing.
There is a smothered giggle, a flurry of footsteps running ahead
of me.

'Who's there?' I call. But when I look down, the stairwell
is thick with shadow. I move carefully, one step at a time.
The music is louder now, almost deafening. 'Velia, ah Velia,
the witch of the wood' – it seems to fill every corner – 'would
I not die for you, dear, if I could.' The walls are rocking. A
foul smell is saturating the hall. I stop and cling to the banister.
My hands are slippery with sweat. At the foot of the stairs,
two brutish figures are locked together, snarling. One looks
up. Her face is disfigured, dark with such baffled fury and
malice I fall back and close my eyes. When I open them the
house is silent. Where the figures wrestled there is only a patch
of sunlight spreading under the front door.

Jersey Road is already changing. The dry cleaner has closed down, the man who exposed himself in the park has given up and gone away, the old lady with the turrets of white hair has vanished as completely as Madame Nightingale. Even the Curtsy Man hasn't been seen lately. Only old Tom still hammers on the common wall, cursing and groaning all night in his single bed till his wife sweeps him out with the leaves next morning. When Jack decides to sell out and retire to his weekender at Woy Woy, we invite him in for a cup of tea, and organise a surprise party with all the neighbours packed into our front courtyard. But he doesn't seem to appreciate it. He is uneasy and after a couple of shandies escapes as soon as he can back into the refuge of his shop. I wonder perhaps if he has sighted the Darkling sisters. Suspiciously, I follow the flick of a grey silk skirt, but it's only the manageress of the new art gallery, and is that the old Edinburgh lady sitting in a wicker chair, eternally smiling, drinking a glass of dry sherry? The neighbours have gone, the glasses and paper plates have been cleared away. I move from room to room, but it isn't my house any more. Perhaps it never was. It belongs to the ghosts, these malevolent spirits who have shown their hand, who won't be kept down but will grow more clamorous every day.

In those last weeks, after we put the house up for sale, when our belongings were all packaged and labelled in Grace Bros cartons, I seemed to hear 'Velia' playing ceremoniously through the empty rooms: 'Velia, ah! Velia, my love and my bride, softly and sadly' . . . softly and sadly, but I am not fooled. The song is triumphant. The Darkling sisters have won. When we sell the console gramophone to the second-hand dealer in Oxford Street I drop the sepia photograph surreptitiously into the cabinet. The dealer tells us he might be able to pick up the missing parts and fix the gramophone up himself, but I feel I ought to warn him. I have visions of

Eleanor and Millie, bead necklaces clicking to their knees, playing their murderous games amongst the cut moquette sofas to tunes from 'The Merry Widow Medley'. I worry too about the young lawyer who has bought the house for his ageing parents, but even if I told him the whole story he wouldn't believe me, just think I was as dotty as Eleanor and Millie.

We buy a three-storey sandstock shell in Darlinghurst and install bars on all the downstairs windows. It had once been an illegal casino, then a down-at-heel boardinghouse. The doors are still numbered but there are no ghosts. Perhaps the transient population never stayed long enough to make any impression. Before we move in a dero shifts from floor to floor, leaving a turd on every landing. There is something homely, even comic, about a turd. It's a memento more tangible and less eerie than the Darkling sisters. The streets of Darlinghurst are like that, everything a mundane overkill, from the proliferation of hookers, female, male, straight and transvestite, to the old alkies shuffling past to the Matthew Talbot. The nights are full of cries from the run-down squats, in the mornings syringes litter the gutters. We live above the streets of the poor listening to the car chasers, the police sirens circling the inner suburbs. Our daughters have grown up and moved away, the young men no longer visit.

My sister comes to visit. Cleaning our mother's tarnished silver-plated teapot, cream jug and sugar bowl, she has copies made of the family photographs and sits up all night making floor-length lace curtains to gentrify the front room. Next morning, brisk and cheerful, she leaves for the airport. 'Goodbye darling,' she calls. As I stand there with tears in my eyes, feeling abandoned, the lace curtains blow in and out in the Southerly Buster. Are we all haunted by the absence of our sisters?

My three-year-old granddaughter fixes me with her grave

dark eyes. 'I am an only child,' she tells me. It seems like a possible solution.

Across the road there is a sign on St Peter's church. 'Don't nurse a grievance, teach it to walk.'

Woollahra
49 Jersey Road
Truly elegant living
Auction on site

A grand Victorian character home with distinctive Italianate facade, gracing one of our best streets.

3/4 bedrooms, formal lounge and dining, family room adjoining magnificent restored kitchen, lock-up shed, rear lane offering great potential.

But do the ghosts still linger; Jack in his white apron ringing up the till, the old Edinburgh lady patting her white hair, old Tom throwing punches, the Curtsy Man flirting his fan?

Leaning out of the attic window, the two little sisters are catching a cardboard crocodile by the tail, but who is the little boy in the wet pants whining softly behind them? Eleanor is strangling Millie at the foot of the stairs, Eva is wrestling the paintbrush from Dora's hand.

My sister, grey-headed now, looking remarkably like our mother, comes walking up the avenue of trees. 'My sister says,' she calls.

The phone rings long distance. 'Silent night, holy night,' sings Madame Nightingale faintly under the falling snow.

MY SISTER
DANCING

ELIZABETH JOLLEY

My Sister Dancing

'**N**ot asleep yet?' the nurse said.

'No. Not yet.'

My sister's face had never been so close to mine before.

'Keep your eyes open,' I told her, 'or they'll come and get you. Go to sleep and keep your eyes open.'

My sister's eyes were very close to mine. They were wide open.

There was hardly room for us in the hospital cot. The nurse had lifted me from my bed. 'I'm putting you in with your sister,' she said, 'she's crying that much, she'll disturb all the others.'

The cot was made of metal and painted white.

'You want a watter?' the nurse leaned over into my sister's sobbing. 'She wants a watter? Watter? Watterdottshiwatt?' the nurse asked me. The nurse wanted my sister to go to sleep, she said. When she came back later the nurse said she *wanted my sister to be asleep.*

'Go to sleep!' I told my sister. 'Go to sleep and keep your eyes open.'

I was five then and my sister was nearly four. We were in the Cottage Hospital to have our tonsils out.

I spat on my finger and smoothed my sister's long dark eyelashes against her cheek. The porter picked her up out of the cot and her head rolled and nestled into his neck as he carried her off.

When it was my turn I was still awake. The porter called me 'old lady'. 'Come along old lady,' he said, and he carried me along a passage past flaring rings of blue flames.

'What are those flames?' I asked him.

'Gas,' he said, 'to boil up the watter in them big sterilizing kettles.'

The porter fastened me on a narrow table with a rubber strap which felt warm. The last thing which I remembered was my foot sinking in a very comfortable way into the soft white-aproned stomach of the nurse who was standing within foot's reach. I have never forgotten, even after so many years, the satisfaction I felt then.

Children are not produced essentially as gifts for each other; but since they come like gifts, unasked for, very often as surprises to the existing children, as something special to be kept and not broken and discarded, I suppose it is true to say that there is no gift which quite equals the gift of a sister born when you are fourteen months old and still holding a precious first place in the household. Even the displacement, which is bound to occur, provides a certain independence and an undisputed status, that of 'the elder sister'.

There came a time in my own life when it became suddenly clear to me that my sister was the one person who had known me for the longest time. With this realisation a number of thoughts followed. One was that the only person who has ever wanted to hear me sing is my sister. In all the things we have shared – earache, chickenpox, measles, sweets, toys, books, love, ambition, shame, fear, to name a few, our two voices have been the most consistently shared in our endless games carried out in dialogue between the characters in our dolls' houses and in a game called Singing in Turns. Some of the dolls' house characters live on still. Joan, a cleaning lady in my sister's dolls' house, did not fit in a bed and so sat all night on a chair. She rattled about on her pink celluloid legs cleaning the dolls' house and gossiping and, without my realising it till later, she became the forerunner of Weekly in my little novel *The Newspaper of Claremont Street*.

'Let's play Singing in Turns.' Often at night we would sing in turns or, if confined to bed, each in separate rooms with an illness, we would sing. We sang songs like 'Drink to Me Only with Thine Eyes' or 'My Bonnie Lies over the Ocean', or hymns, 'Lead Kindly Light' or, 'All Things Bright and Beautiful'. There was a song called 'The Wild Woodland Cherry Tree' which had in the first line the phrase: *so lissom so tall*. Not knowing what *lissom* was, the word gave the song a magical quality. We did not know the whole song but were content with the first few lines. Often, pitching the first notes too high, the singer would be obliged to stop and start again on a lower note. The audience of one was quite uncritical.

Another shared experience was that of our father reading aloud to us. He, during a childhood illness, would stand out on the landing taking care not to enter the rooms where the infection lurked. He was a teacher and could not go to school carrying our germs. He read then in the deep voice he kept for the boys at school.

A very strong memory among the many cherished memories of *sister* is the shared convalescence, in candlelight very often, with the remaking of old familiar jigsaw puzzles or setting up the shabby magic of a book which contained scenes for plays. These could be performed with little paper characters pushed on the stage with strips of cardboard. Cinderella was one.

During convalescence we were given plates of sliced up oranges. The plates sat on the hearth rug in the middle of all the dolls' clothes. The days were spent at the window watching builders next door. The builders made cement and ran up and down ladders with cement and bricks on little boards balanced on their heads. We called one of the builders Dozing John because we saw him having forty winks in the sun. In imagination we talked to Dozing John and made cement for him. We told him about ourselves and made plans to run away with him. I remember my sister packed a case with dolls' clothes in readiness. Perhaps I did the same but have forgotten.

We shared germs too. At that time a lot of emphasis was given to germs. Professor Winifred Cullis (whose wireless lessons I loved – human biology) spoke of the risk of sharing a cup or biting someone else's apple. She said that germs grew if you slept in your vest. Every night we took off all our clothes and standing on the landing at the top of the stairs we shook out all the germs from each article of clothing. The bath was another thing we shared. We took turns quite strictly to have either the rounded end or the end with the plug and the taps.

So many things in turn, housework for one thing:

'It's your turn to do the wiping up.'

'No it isn't it's your turn.'

or; 'You're being called to set the table.'

'No I'm not. It's you being called . . .'

We often, in anger, pulled each other's hair. I have a memory of a handful of my hair being torn out by the roots. But perhaps this was the other way round!

We chose records in turn, taking turns to wind up the gramophone. My mother sometimes had a chance to choose. She chose *'Tales from the Vienna Woods'*. We had a whole pile of records *'Gretchen am Spinnrade'*, *'Heidenröslein'*, *'Auf dem Wasser zu Singen'*, *'Der Erl König'*, the third movement of Mozart's symphony number thirty-nine, the Anvil chorus and the Soldiers' chorus from *'Il Trovatore'* and so on. These records were all seventy-eights and it was possible to have one movement from a symphony without the rest of it. So, though we knew the third movement of the Mozart symphony, neither of us would have recognised it if we had heard the beginning.

In the line, *Erl König hat mir ein Leid getan* and during Azucena's aria, in which she discloses, in an ever-deepening

contralto, that Manrico is the Count's long lost brother, I hid
my face so that my sister would not see tears spilling down
my cheeks.

We had spotted frocks, matching each other, frocks with lines
and squares on them, embroidered rosebud frocks with
reversible ribbons at the waist, frocks with frills and puffed
sleeves, and one summer, our mother had our hair shingled
and we each had a pair of shorts. No one else in the street
had shorts. An old lady passing our front garden looked
through a gap in the hedge. Are you two boys or girls, she
wanted to know.

'I'm Monica Elizabeth,' I explained, 'and she's Madelaine
Winifred, we're boys.'

Later on, being too old for Shirley Temple frocks, we each
had a Deanna Durbin dress.

Following the sophistication of the film-star fashion
dresses, Marie Stopes appeared on the brush and comb shelf
inside our wardrobe. We read the book secretly and, with a
silent sort of agreement, we hid the book so that our mother
should not see it. It never occurred to either of us then that
she, hoping I suppose, to offer enlightenment, had placed the
book where we would see it and read it.

Perhaps the conspiracy of jealousy is most powerful when
it is between, I should say *shared*, between sisters.

The summer after the summer of the shingled heads and
the shorts we were taken, by our father, to visit relatives who
lived on farms in Wiltshire. At Coopers Farm we discovered
a little girl called Betsy. Fair-skinned with rosy cheeks and
golden curls, she wore sturdy pinafores over her serge dresses,
black knee-length stockings and lace-up farm boots, also
black. Next to her, in our crêpe de chine summer frocks which
had low round necks and dropped waists, and our feet bare
in Oxford sandals, we were not at all sure how we stood with
her.

'I don't like Betsy,' I told my father.

'Why not?'

I did not know how to answer this. 'Well,' I said, 'she can't read.'

'You read to her,' my father said, 'with your finger under the words to show them to her.' This should have made me feel better.

'Shan't!' I said.

My father took us, all three, to the museum in Salisbury and began as always to make a lesson out of everything. Especially he seemed to be showing Betsy everything.

'Have a look at this, Betsy' and 'Betsy, look! Have you ever seen anything like this?' My sister and I did not want to be alongside this Betsy. We had already had a slow race with her eating a banana each. The idea was to eat slowly and the one who had some banana left when the others had eaten all theirs won.

'We've eaten all our banana,' in silent agreement my sister and I folded our apparently empty banana skins over, flapping them at Betsy.

'Empty banana peels. See?'

So Betsy ate all hers, finished it up, and with horrid triumph we revealed that we both had some left.

'We've won. We've won.'

Our father seemed to be concentrating all his attention on this Betsy from Coopers Farm. Who was she anyway? Who did she think she was? The museum was hideously dull. We began to jump over the glass cases which were low down on the floor. First my sister jumped and then I ran and jumped. Backwards and forwards over these show cases, never mind what they contained, just old rocks. I shouted 'Heads!' Over the glass, jump, back over the glass, jump. This would teach our Dad to prefer Betsy to us if anything would. We were quite out of breath with our jumping. I found I could land with quite a heavy thud . . .

A lady dressed in a uniform came over to us. We had not noticed her before. She said we were to stop the noise and that jumping the exhibits was not allowed and would we go outside immediately and wait till our father had finished showing the other little girl the things in the museum.

'That woman,' my sister said, when we waited outside on the steps of the museum, 'that woman, she's a woman and a half and she needs cutting up a bit.'

Together, discovering their particular fears, we tormented our Austrian and French governesses with earthworms and spiders. Rushing through long wet grass we terrified ourselves simultaneously by getting our sandals full of squashed slugs.

It was when I was sent to boarding school at the age of eleven that, as well as having to become accustomed to an entirely different life, I missed my sister dreadfully. I began then to write stories for her which I sent home in my Sunday letter.

It came as something of a shock to me many years later to receive a reproach from my sister for having left her in the way that I did at the time. That *she* suffered from my being sent away to school had not been clear to me. In my own struggle to overcome shyness, loneliness, homesickness (that most bitter and wasteful of all 'sickness') and to contend with a cruel bullying prevalent in boarding schools then, I had thought of her as being fortunate in being at home still – in privacy and surrounded by all our treasures. I never thought of her in a pathetic position, that of being *left alone* at home.

My sister (for reasons best known to my mother and father) did not come to the school till the first year of the war. The school was in the country and a number of young brothers and sisters became boarders because it was considered to be safe from air raids.

When my sister was at school I experienced something I have never forgotten and that was (and is) pride. I was so proud of her, my sister. My little sister, who had remained little in my mind, had grown up to be dainty and pretty. She walked with a springing step. She was loved at once by the friends I had made.

In the folk-dancing class on Thursday evenings (which I never liked) she learned all the dances. She danced with a neatness and a delicate energy making the dances, which previously I thought of as silly and meaningless, into something special. I saw for the first time an expression of human emotion and life in the movements of the dance.

In order to watch her, and only her, I volunteered to be in charge of the gramophone, winding it up, turning the records over and changing the needle. I sat every Thursday evening watching the ways in which my sister moved to and fro and round and round. I watched carefully the ways in which she moved her hands, her head and her feet.

My sister dancing was better than any of the others. She was perfect.

'That's my sister dancing,' I wanted to say to the others. 'Watch my sister, look at the way she turns. See, she hardly seems to touch the floor.'

I did not speak of this aloud.

That's my sister, I said somewhere inside myself. I could not take my eyes off my sister dancing.

A QUESTION OF UPBRINGING

Once, years ago, my sister wanted to sell me her bicycle.

'Sisters do not buy and sell with each other,' my mother said, 'sisters share.'

A *Question of Upbringing*: a general observation perhaps when visiting, perhaps at a dinner party . . .

Sisters brought up, close in age, by the same mother, have some things in common which can be observed to persist throughout childhood and into later years even if one, giving herself an androgynous nickname, is an adult tomboy and the other is quite clearly small-boned and delicately built with a penchant for beauty preparations, jewellery and fashionable clothes. For example, both women independently of one another will save and fold a piece of greaseproof paper from the inside of the cereal packet and, with exactly the same speed and exactly the same hand and finger movements put it away, allegedly for further use, in a kitchen cupboard overflowing already with similar careful foldings.

More important perhaps is the extent of the shared agitation and dismay when the first course of a dinner party is being cleared in either sister's house (or in someone else's house where both sisters are present) and a fork tips and falls from a partly empty plate which is being removed. The sisters immediately exchange impatient glances of concern tinged with more than a little lack of tolerance over this accidental carelessness. One of two things happens – either both women are on their knees examining the carpet and hastily removing any traces of dropped food or one sister calls frowning to the other, who is also frowning, after retrieving the lost fork quickly, saying that there's no harm done to the table cloth or to the carpet . . .

The folding and the frowning and the momentary simultaneous loss of tolerance have been handed from mother to daughters to be shared by sisters.

To see this kind of thing you have to stare.

Perhaps like many writers I do stare at people. It has been said that writers are born watching and staring. It is something they can't help. A quotation from Morley Callaghan sent to me by the Melbourne poet Fairlie Szyacinski goes like this: 'There is only one trait that marks the writer. He is always watching. It's a kind of trick of mind and he is born with it.'

My Father's Sister

Sister might not necessarily mean one's own sister.

My father had to look after his younger sister, he told me. Elder brothers and elder sisters, he said, must always look after the younger ones. He had to take his sister to the Elementary School every day. He was not fond of going to school himself. On one occasion he returned home telling his mother that the school gates were locked because the school had burned down during the night. This was before his sister was old enough to be taken to school. His mother (later on to be my grandmother) said she would very much like to see a burned-down school. And, putting on her hat and coat, she walked him straight back down to the school where the bell was ringing and the children, in their separate playgrounds, were lining up to go in.

My father's sister was called Daisy (she, later, was my Aunt Daisy). In taking Daisy to school, my father explained, he adopted a method of getting her there as quickly as he could. He was always afraid of being late. (LATE spells late, I told my own sister when I was hurrying her along to school. I had, it seemed, inherited my father's fear of being late. Perhaps I should explain here that we did have a short time in Mixed Infants before my father arranged for us to have governesses at home.)

But to go back to my father getting his sister to school. He hooked an arm round her neck, he told me, and set off at a steady trot with her held fast in the crook of his arm, their metal-tipped boots sounding like little horses along the pavement. Sometimes, by accident, they kicked and bruised each other's ankles. She wore, he remembered, a round knitted cap with loose woollen tassels which he could feel against his neck. On arrival at the school he used to push her hard, he described it as a shove, through the gate which had an archway marked GIRLS in big iron letters. And then he would run off, as if unrelated to her, head down, his responsibility shed, to a similar gateway, arched in iron, and marked BOYS.

My father felt responsible for his sister all his life in spite of her sometimes uncompromising attitude towards the woman (*a foreigner*) he chose to be his wife. He did not expect her 'to speak up' for him, this sister, when she stood wordless, half hidden in the thick curtains of the cold room they called the drawing room, peering out to the street where the neighbours had gathered to watch when he was being disowned, in public, by his father (later to be my grandfather) and turned out of the house with only a shilling, for being a conscientious objector and for being in prison during the Great War.

My father always, when telling this, explained that it was the disgrace of being in prison which had upset his father so much. It was not so much the reason for it. He used to say too, by way of an alleviation, that a shilling was worth far more in those days. For example, a bundle of candles cost three ha'pence, a large loaf was threepence, milk a penny, and so on.

My father found excuses for his sister for every accusation levelled at her by my mother (her sister-in-law) and he visited her every Saturday for years. She always had worries and work waiting for him. He returned home white-faced and exhausted.

I suppose my father's sister never was able to like her sister-in-law, my mother. Though I do recall conspiratorial closings of the bedroom door, either at my grandmother's house or in our own house, for discussions over the Christmas dolls, the chosen books, dresses and other presents. And I have an indelible memory of my aunt and my mother, the sisters-in-law, sitting together one afternoon, a dark afternoon, and my father's sister cried and cried and my mother, with not enough English for the occasion, tried to comfort her. I must have been about eight then and I can remember wishing my father would come home from taking the boys at school to the swimming baths or down a coal mine or something of that sort. In spite of that afternoon, as time passed, the sisters-in-law did not improve in their feelings towards each other.

In fact, the biggest insult hurled between us (my sister and me) was for one to say that the other was 'getting like Aunt Daisy'. My mother took part in this with her own critical remarks intended for our good: 'Don't eat like your Aunt Daisy' and 'Don't sit like your Aunt Daisy' 'Don't *do anything* like your Aunt Daisy' and about clothes, the worst thing that could be said was: 'That's the kind of *thing* Aunt Daisy would choose'.

After the death of my grandmother, my father's sister had a housekeeper companion for many years. She was a true daughter of the canal barges, sharp-tongued, energetic, quick at mental arithmetic and spelling; she was knowledgeable about things medical, geographical, historical, political and personal. She was a small thin woman with a pile of white hair and a voice. Miss Clayton and my father's sister got on satisfactorily together by frequent repetitions of that certain emotional release which follows on the heels of an all-time, all-encompassing row. These two, they had many such rows either when they were alone together or in the presence of company or even when there was simply an audience of one. These rows, violent and at screaming pitch, in an agitation of rocking chairs, came unheralded and ended quickly in low voices, soothing moans and endearments uttered from these same rocking chairs which gradually subsided on either side of the hearth.

My mother (the sister-in-law), all her life, could not stand the sight of a rocking chair.

My father stopped visiting his sister quite suddenly. He never explained to anyone why he no longer visited her house.

When my father's sister died she died in her rocking chair with a book in her lap and a cup of tea at her elbow. Quite peaceful, Miss Clayton told my father who, in the event of death, was obliged, as he said, to go over there.

He was required to clear up her things.

His sister having bought an annuity for herself previously with what my mother (her sister-in-law) declared was mostly my father's share of the inheritance after the death of, first, his father and then his mother, there was no money left for anyone.

The sad part about it was, my father said later, there was a houseful of possessions, furniture, books, pictures, clothes, knives and forks and plates and cups and photographs all of which were *treasures* to her but unwanted by anyone else. He gave away what he could and had to have enormous bonfires for the rest. There was, for example, a whole cabinet of babies' dresses carefully embroidered, some with smocking, and trimmed with lace by her girls at school. She had been a sewing teacher. She was always very proud of the collection of what she called 'my girls' work'. The babies' dresses were, by this time, discoloured and marked in places with mildew; some were actually rotten.

Even when all the clearing up was finished my father still did not say what had made him stop his weekly visits after continuing them regularly for all those years in the face of my mother's outbursts of anger and reproach.

Before I go on I must explain that my father's sister, my mother's sister-in-law, was a very kind aunty to me. I understand that now. She was kind and fond in the only ways she knew how to be. She always sent postcards from her holiday travellings and letters, especially letters with promises: '*if you and your sister will come on Saturday you will be able to have the new picture books I have for you both.*' That sort of thing. I see now that she was lonely and her letters were often pathetic attempts to entice us to visit. It was she who sent the schoolgirl stories to me at boarding school: *Treacle of St Mikes* and *The*

Dimsie Omnibus. The possession of these and some others ensured my popularity for quite a time.

My father often said that the people who were the hardest to love were the ones who needed loving most. I see now that he was sorry for his sister and saw her as a person all alone, unloved and, what was worse, having no one of her own to love. And that was why he went every Saturday on the early train returning at night exhausted after digging her garden or mending something in the house, very often something which should have been discarded and replaced. But what tired him most, my mother would argue, were the tirades of complaints and worries. My mother often remarked that her sister-in-law was like a dog with a bone. She would describe the dog worrying the bone, putting the bone down and taking it up again to shake it first one way and then the other way. She said her sister-in-law would even, like a dog, bury her bone in order to dig it up once more and start worrying it all over again. My father, after one of his Saturday visits to his sister, once asked me what he could suggest she should buy for inexpensive presents for her friends at Christmas because she was worrying about Christmas so much and it was then still only June.

It was only much later on, after many years, that I understood why, without saying anything to anyone, he stopped visiting his sister. He made this big change in his life and in hers because of me. It was out of loyalty and love for me that he gave up his sister. A great part of her weekly tirade, for a number of years, would have been about me.

It was like this. I had not seen my father's sister, my aunt, for some years when she called unexpectedly to see me one day. I was working then as housekeeper in a large house belonging to a wealthy factory owner. I had my own apartment there and a part of the garden was set aside as mine.

Without touching her tea or the bread and butter I offered

her, she began to explain in very carefully articulated words that, because of the way in which I was living and must have lived (this with a sidelong glance at the baby clothes arranged for airing along the fireguard) she had, in her words, been obliged to cut me out of her will, completely out of her will.

The surprise of this was not in connection with any possible gift being withheld, it was more to do with the fact that she had planned to make a long and awkward journey by train and bus for this particular reason, this special intention. The sudden intensification of my own feelings of loneliness was a surprise too. I was already alone. I was accustomed to the idea that I was alone, but her words caused an extra emptiness, that of being removed from belonging to a family.

Immediately, perhaps with the aid of a cultivated practice of self-protection, consolation and rescue, without really thinking, I told her: 'Please don't worry about me, I have been well provided for.'

'Don't tell Dad,' I said later when visiting my mother (my father's sister's sister-in-law).

My mother said that it could be considered a great comfort for us both that the Georgian silver teaspoons I was meant to inherit from my grandmother via Aunt Daisy would hang like a great weight round her neck . . . She paused suitably in her finger-pointing pronouncement to let all the possible horrors contained in this image to be continued in the imagination.

'Don't tell Dad,' I said again, not thinking that of course my aunt would tell him herself, rail at him, have him on the mat, worrying the subject – the dog worrying the bone – never giving him any peace, wanting to know who was providing for me, what sort of people did his daughter know and mix with and what dark world of sin was she being paid to inhabit.

Not thinking, I said again to my mother, 'Don't tell Dad.' She said she wouldn't but of course she did because, as I should have known by then, she always told my father everything.

And it was after this that he stopped going to see his sister. And I never saw her again either.

I prefer not to remember my aunt, my father's sister, in this way. I like best to think of them, the two of them, as children, as brother and sister, playing a game my father described once when he was making cocoa one evening for my sister and me. The game he said was called horses and carts. They played the game at the kitchen table. They had a preserving jar, with a lid, full of nuts and bolts and nails and screws. They said the kitchen table was the road and they arranged the screws and the nuts and bolts all dotted up and down the table – dot-dot-dotty-dot along the table, they were the horses and carts going along the road, passing each other, turning in the road, stopping and starting – this game, my father explained, he played with his sister.

Years later, long after the deaths of my father and his sister, the memory of his telling about the game came to me during a night when I was trying to write a story. I gave the game to the man in the story, as his childhood memory, and events in the story are paralleled by the events in the boy's game.

It is only now while my mind is on sisters, on my father's sister, that I see that, as in *the lives of the obscure*, being supplied *first with gilt-edged note paper and then with baby linen* and that hiding out in the parklands of the wealthy was not what she had in mind for me during all the years when I had been, as in the promise of Isaiah, graven on the palms of her hands, cherished there and not forgotten. She came to visit me that day because she was concerned and honest and because she loved me.

I am here now never having said anything more to her after those words which jumped from me in defence and which were not true.

I am sitting here remembering all kinds of things like the times when I was with my sister, warm in our nightdresses by the hearth, playing with new building blocks. Each block had an animal, a goat, a lamb, a cockerel, a cow, on it and, when a special little string, attached to the block, was pulled, the sound of the particular animal emerged mysteriously from somewhere inside the block. There was, as well, a tiny stove which had a spirit lamp inside. Real vegetables could be cut up and boiled in proper little saucepans. Real tea could be made for the dolls when the water came to the boil in the tiny kettle . . .

My father's sister making the difficult journey, inarticulate in her inability to reach and protect, became judge and critic.

What remains from all this is my father's love for his sister, complicated of course. And, of course, there was their helplessness.

Gillian Mears is 29 years old and grew up in northern New South Wales, where she is again living. She has published two collections of short stories and a novel, *The Mint Lawn*, which won the Vogel/Australia award.

Beth Yahp was born in Malaysia and now lives in Sydney. Her novel, *The Crocodile Fury*, was published in 1992.

Helen Garner was born and lives in Melbourne. She writes novels, stories, screenplays and various kinds of journalism. Her most recent book is *Cosmo Cosmolino*.

Drusilla Modjeska's books include *Exiles at Home* (1981) and *Poppy* (1990). She lives in Sydney.

Dorothy Hewett was born in Perth, Western Australia, in 1923. Her most recent publications are an autobiography, *Wildcard*, Vol. 1 of her collected plays, and a novel, *The Toucher*. Her fifth poetry collection, *Peninsula*, will appear in March 1994.

Elizabeth Jolley is the author of ten novels, three short story collections and two books of non-fiction, of which her most recent is *Diary of a Weekend Farmer*. Her latest novel, *The Georges' Wife*, will be published shortly. She lives in Perth, where she teaches writing at the Curtin University of Technology.